This Coffee Tasting Journal belongs to:

Dedication

This Coffee Tasting Journal is dedicated to all the coffee lovers out there. The ones who wake up in the morning to drink their favorite drip coffee, espresso, or fancy coffee drink!

Coffee is an obsession for so many around the world, because it gives us energy in the morning (and for some, all day!) and makes us feel good. This Coffee Tasting Journal is dedicated to all those who need their caffeine fix!

Drink up!

How to Use This Coffee Tasting Journal:

This Coffee Tasting Journal is a great way for coffee drinkers to not only track which coffees they try, but also find out what your favorite type of coffee is – from the flavour, to the milk, aroma, brew method, etc.

Inside you'll find each entry includes space for tracking:

General Information – Name, Roastery, Brew Method, Grind, Extras, Origin, Sample. This is a great snapshot to see what kind of beans, from where, and how you make them affects the coffee that you like.

Serving Type – Mark whether you're making a Casual, Espresso, Cappuccino, Latte, Mocha, Macchiato, etc. Many different types of drinks, so try them all!

Color – A sliding scale you can mark whether it looks light or dark.

Flavor Wheel – A great way to visualize how the coffee tastes.

Additional Notes – Plenty of space to list ideas and reflections on your drink.

Final Rating – Rate several different aspects of your coffee so you can know whether to make it again or not.

Enjoy!

✿ NAME	
▦ ROASTERY	☕ BREW METHOD
⚙ GRIND	🧁 EXTRAS
🌍 ORIGIN	📅 SAMPLED

SERVING TYPE

CASUAL	ESPRESSO	CAPPUCCINO	LATTE	MOCHA	MACCHIATO	OTHER
☕	☕	☕	🥤	☕	🥛	☕
☐	☐	☐	☐	☐	☐	☐

COLOR

LIGHT   DARK

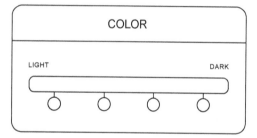

FLAVOR WHEEL

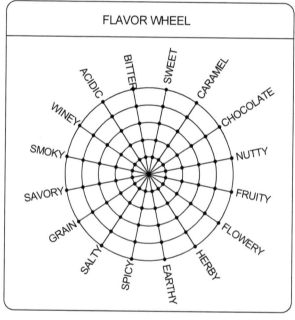

ADDITIONAL NOTES

FINAL RATING

◉ APPEARANCE		☆☆☆☆☆
🌿 AROMA		☆☆☆☆☆
☕ TASTE		☆☆☆☆☆
💧 CREMA		☆☆☆☆☆
✍ OVERALL RATING		☆☆☆☆☆

🫘 NAME	
🏭 ROASTERY	☕ BREW METHOD
⚙️ GRIND	🧁 EXTRAS
🌍 ORIGIN	📅 SAMPLED

SERVING TYPE

CASUAL	ESPRESSO	CAPPUCCINO	LATTE	MOCHA	MACCHIATO	OTHER
☐	☐	☐	☐	☐	☐	☐

COLOR

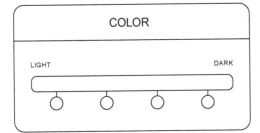

LIGHT   DARK

ADDITIONAL NOTES

FLAVOR WHEEL

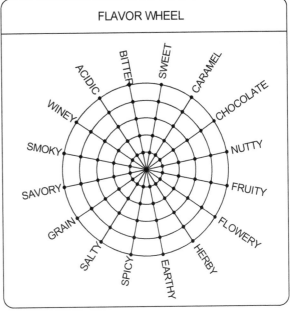

ACIDIC · BITTER · SWEET · CARAMEL · CHOCOLATE · NUTTY · FRUITY · FLOWERY · HERBY · EARTHY · SPICY · SALTY · GRAIN · SAVORY · SMOKY · WINEY

FINAL RATING

🍩 APPEARANCE	☆☆☆☆☆
🌿 AROMA	☆☆☆☆☆
☕ TASTE	☆☆☆☆☆
💧 CREMA	☆☆☆☆☆
🤲 OVERALL RATING	☆☆☆☆☆

NAME

ROASTERY	BREW METHOD
GRIND	EXTRAS
ORIGIN	SAMPLED

SERVING TYPE

CASUAL	ESPRESSO	CAPPUCCINO	LATTE	MOCHA	MACCHIATO	OTHER
☐	☐	☐	☐	☐	☐	☐

COLOR

LIGHT   DARK

FLAVOR WHEEL

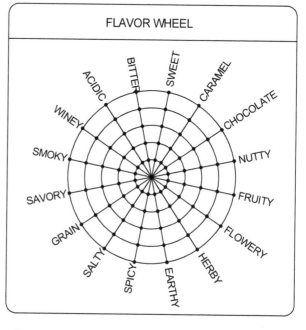

ACIDIC, BITTER, SWEET, CARAMEL, CHOCOLATE, NUTTY, FRUITY, FLOWERY, HERBY, EARTHY, SPICY, SALTY, GRAIN, SAVORY, SMOKY, WINEY

ADDITIONAL NOTES

FINAL RATING

APPEARANCE	☆☆☆☆☆
AROMA	☆☆☆☆☆
TASTE	☆☆☆☆☆
CREMA	☆☆☆☆☆
OVERALL RATING	☆☆☆☆☆

NAME

ROASTERY	BREW METHOD
GRIND	EXTRAS
ORIGIN	SAMPLED

SERVING TYPE

CASUAL	ESPRESSO	CAPPUCCINO	LATTE	MOCHA	MACCHIATO	OTHER
☐	☐	☐	☐	☐	☐	☐

COLOR

LIGHT — DARK

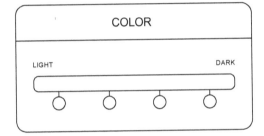

FLAVOR WHEEL

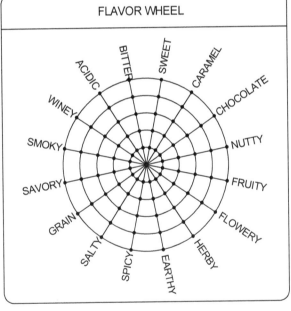

BITTER, SWEET, CARAMEL, ACIDIC, CHOCOLATE, WINEY, NUTTY, SMOKY, FRUITY, SAVORY, FLOWERY, GRAIN, HERBY, SALTY, SPICY, EARTHY

ADDITIONAL NOTES

FINAL RATING

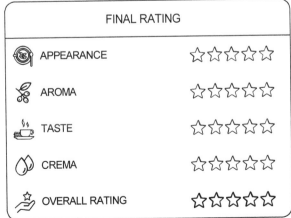

APPEARANCE	☆☆☆☆☆
AROMA	☆☆☆☆☆
TASTE	☆☆☆☆☆
CREMA	☆☆☆☆☆
OVERALL RATING	☆☆☆☆☆

NAME

ROASTERY	BREW METHOD
GRIND	EXTRAS
ORIGIN	SAMPLED

SERVING TYPE

CASUAL	ESPRESSO	CAPPUCCINO	LATTE	MOCHA	MACCHIATO	OTHER
☐	☐	☐	☐	☐	☐	☐

COLOR

LIGHT — DARK

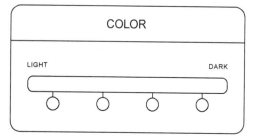

FLAVOR WHEEL

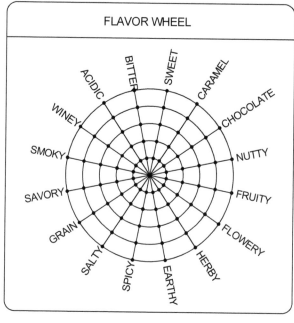

ACIDIC · BITTER · SWEET · CARAMEL · CHOCOLATE · NUTTY · FRUITY · FLOWERY · HERBY · EARTHY · SPICY · SALTY · GRAIN · SAVORY · SMOKY · WINEY

ADDITIONAL NOTES

FINAL RATING

APPEARANCE	☆☆☆☆☆
AROMA	☆☆☆☆☆
TASTE	☆☆☆☆☆
CREMA	☆☆☆☆☆
OVERALL RATING	☆☆☆☆☆

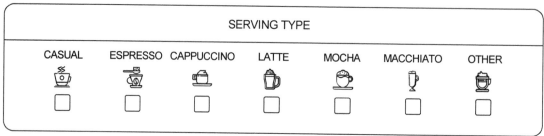
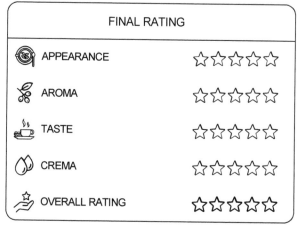

NAME

ROASTERY	BREW METHOD
GRIND	EXTRAS
ORIGIN	SAMPLED

SERVING TYPE

CASUAL	ESPRESSO	CAPPUCCINO	LATTE	MOCHA	MACCHIATO	OTHER
☐	☐	☐	☐	☐	☐	☐

COLOR

LIGHT   DARK

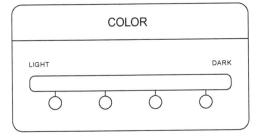

FLAVOR WHEEL

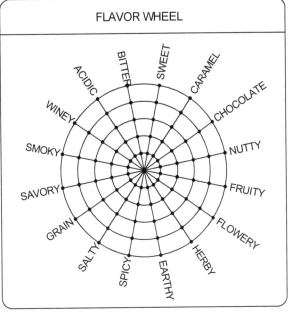

BITTER · SWEET · CARAMEL · CHOCOLATE · NUTTY · FRUITY · FLOWERY · HERBY · EARTHY · SPICY · SALTY · GRAIN · SAVORY · SMOKY · WINEY · ACIDIC

ADDITIONAL NOTES

FINAL RATING

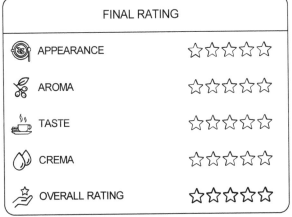

APPEARANCE	☆☆☆☆☆
AROMA	☆☆☆☆☆
TASTE	☆☆☆☆☆
CREMA	☆☆☆☆☆
OVERALL RATING	☆☆☆☆☆

NAME

ROASTERY	BREW METHOD
GRIND	EXTRAS
ORIGIN	SAMPLED

SERVING TYPE

CASUAL	ESPRESSO	CAPPUCCINO	LATTE	MOCHA	MACCHIATO	OTHER
☐	☐	☐	☐	☐	☐	☐

COLOR

LIGHT   DARK

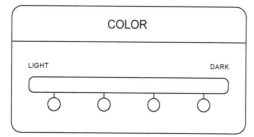

FLAVOR WHEEL

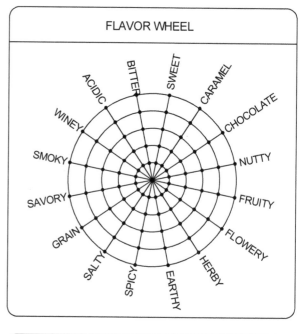

ADDITIONAL NOTES

FINAL RATING

APPEARANCE		☆☆☆☆☆
AROMA		☆☆☆☆☆
TASTE		☆☆☆☆☆
CREMA		☆☆☆☆☆
OVERALL RATING		☆☆☆☆☆

NAME

ROASTERY	BREW METHOD
GRIND	EXTRAS
ORIGIN	SAMPLED

SERVING TYPE

CASUAL	ESPRESSO	CAPPUCCINO	LATTE	MOCHA	MACCHIATO	OTHER
☐	☐	☐	☐	☐	☐	☐

COLOR

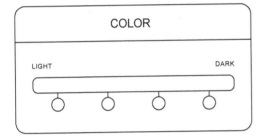

LIGHT   DARK

FLAVOR WHEEL

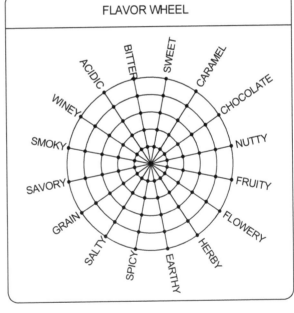

BITTER · SWEET · CARAMEL · CHOCOLATE · NUTTY · FRUITY · FLOWERY · HERBY · EARTHY · SPICY · SALTY · GRAIN · SAVORY · SMOKY · WINEY · ACIDIC

ADDITIONAL NOTES

FINAL RATING

APPEARANCE	☆☆☆☆☆
AROMA	☆☆☆☆☆
TASTE	☆☆☆☆☆
CREMA	☆☆☆☆☆
OVERALL RATING	☆☆☆☆☆

NAME

ROASTERY	BREW METHOD
GRIND	EXTRAS
ORIGIN	SAMPLED

SERVING TYPE

CASUAL	ESPRESSO	CAPPUCCINO	LATTE	MOCHA	MACCHIATO	OTHER
☐	☐	☐	☐	☐	☐	☐

COLOR

LIGHT — DARK

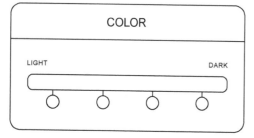

FLAVOR WHEEL

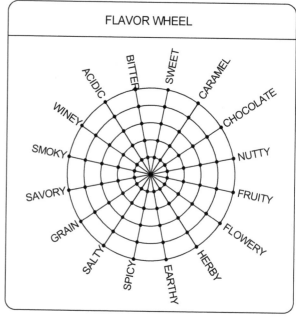

BITTER · SWEET · CARAMEL · CHOCOLATE · NUTTY · FRUITY · FLOWERY · HERBY · EARTHY · SPICY · SALTY · GRAIN · SAVORY · SMOKY · WINEY · ACIDIC

ADDITIONAL NOTES

FINAL RATING

APPEARANCE	☆☆☆☆☆
AROMA	☆☆☆☆☆
TASTE	☆☆☆☆☆
CREMA	☆☆☆☆☆
OVERALL RATING	☆☆☆☆☆

NAME

ROASTERY	BREW METHOD
GRIND	EXTRAS
ORIGIN	SAMPLED

SERVING TYPE

CASUAL	ESPRESSO	CAPPUCCINO	LATTE	MOCHA	MACCHIATO	OTHER
☐	☐	☐	☐	☐	☐	☐

COLOR

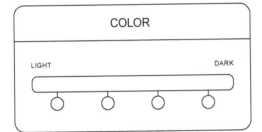

LIGHT · DARK

ADDITIONAL NOTES

FLAVOR WHEEL

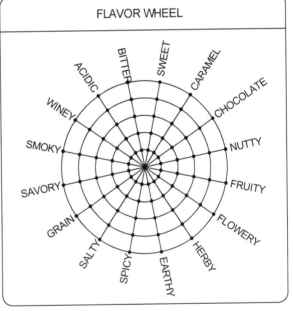

ACIDIC · BITTER · SWEET · CARAMEL · CHOCOLATE · WINEY · SMOKY · NUTTY · SAVORY · FRUITY · GRAIN · FLOWERY · SALTY · SPICY · EARTHY · HERBY

FINAL RATING

APPEARANCE	☆☆☆☆☆
AROMA	☆☆☆☆☆
TASTE	☆☆☆☆☆
CREMA	☆☆☆☆☆
OVERALL RATING	☆☆☆☆☆

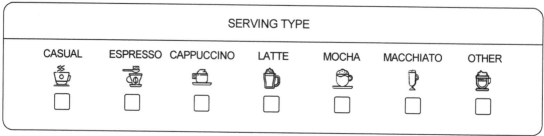

NAME

ROASTERY	BREW METHOD
GRIND	EXTRAS
ORIGIN	SAMPLED

SERVING TYPE

CASUAL	ESPRESSO	CAPPUCCINO	LATTE	MOCHA	MACCHIATO	OTHER
☐	☐	☐	☐	☐	☐	☐

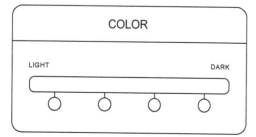

COLOR

LIGHT   DARK

FLAVOR WHEEL

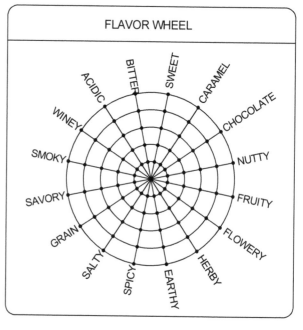

ACIDIC · BITTER · SWEET · CARAMEL · CHOCOLATE · NUTTY · FRUITY · FLOWERY · HERBY · EARTHY · SPICY · SALTY · GRAIN · SAVORY · SMOKY · WINEY

ADDITIONAL NOTES

FINAL RATING

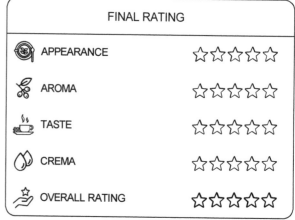

APPEARANCE	☆☆☆☆☆
AROMA	☆☆☆☆☆
TASTE	☆☆☆☆☆
CREMA	☆☆☆☆☆
OVERALL RATING	☆☆☆☆☆

NAME

ROASTERY	BREW METHOD
GRIND	EXTRAS
ORIGIN	SAMPLED

SERVING TYPE

CASUAL	ESPRESSO	CAPPUCCINO	LATTE	MOCHA	MACCHIATO	OTHER
☐	☐	☐	☐	☐	☐	☐

COLOR

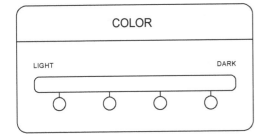

LIGHT · · · · DARK

FLAVOR WHEEL

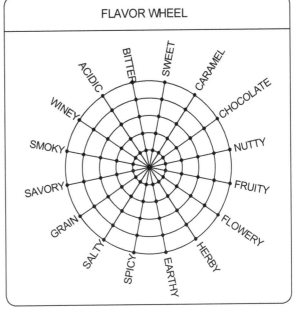

ADDITIONAL NOTES

FINAL RATING

APPEARANCE	☆☆☆☆☆
AROMA	☆☆☆☆☆
TASTE	☆☆☆☆☆
CREMA	☆☆☆☆☆
OVERALL RATING	☆☆☆☆☆

NAME

ROASTERY	BREW METHOD
GRIND	EXTRAS
ORIGIN	SAMPLED

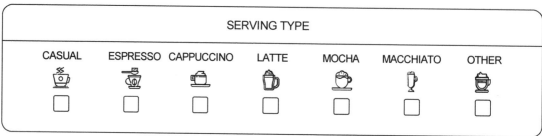

SERVING TYPE

CASUAL	ESPRESSO	CAPPUCCINO	LATTE	MOCHA	MACCHIATO	OTHER
☐	☐	☐	☐	☐	☐	☐

COLOR

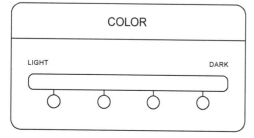

LIGHT   DARK

FLAVOR WHEEL

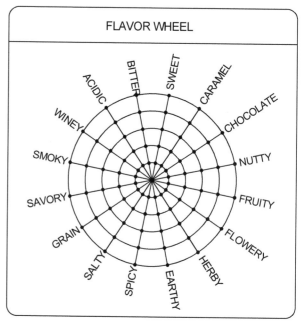

ADDITIONAL NOTES

FINAL RATING

APPEARANCE	☆☆☆☆☆
AROMA	☆☆☆☆☆
TASTE	☆☆☆☆☆
CREMA	☆☆☆☆☆
OVERALL RATING	☆☆☆☆☆

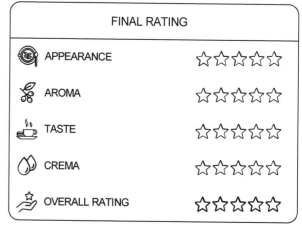

NAME	
ROASTERY	BREW METHOD
GRIND	EXTRAS
ORIGIN	SAMPLED

SERVING TYPE

CASUAL	ESPRESSO	CAPPUCCINO	LATTE	MOCHA	MACCHIATO	OTHER
☐	☐	☐	☐	☐	☐	☐

COLOR

LIGHT — DARK

FLAVOR WHEEL

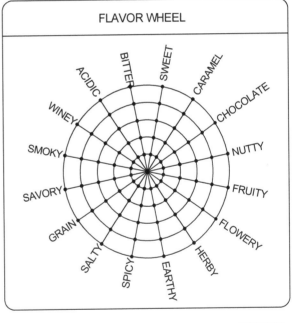

ACIDIC, BITTER, SWEET, CARAMEL, CHOCOLATE, NUTTY, FRUITY, FLOWERY, HERBY, EARTHY, SPICY, SALTY, GRAIN, SAVORY, SMOKY, WINEY

ADDITIONAL NOTES

FINAL RATING

APPEARANCE	☆☆☆☆☆
AROMA	☆☆☆☆☆
TASTE	☆☆☆☆☆
CREMA	☆☆☆☆☆
OVERALL RATING	☆☆☆☆☆

NAME

ROASTERY	BREW METHOD
GRIND	EXTRAS
ORIGIN	SAMPLED

SERVING TYPE

CASUAL	ESPRESSO	CAPPUCCINO	LATTE	MOCHA	MACCHIATO	OTHER
☐	☐	☐	☐	☐	☐	☐

COLOR

LIGHT   DARK

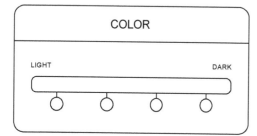

FLAVOR WHEEL

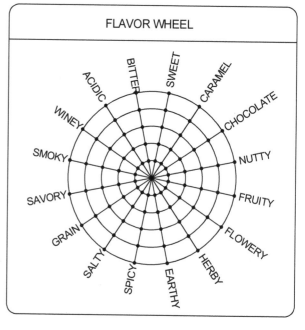

ACIDIC, BITTER, SWEET, CARAMEL, CHOCOLATE, NUTTY, FRUITY, FLOWERY, HERBY, EARTHY, SPICY, SALTY, GRAIN, SAVORY, SMOKY, WINEY

ADDITIONAL NOTES

FINAL RATING

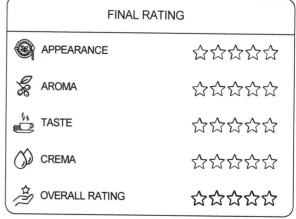

APPEARANCE	☆☆☆☆☆
AROMA	☆☆☆☆☆
TASTE	☆☆☆☆☆
CREMA	☆☆☆☆☆
OVERALL RATING	☆☆☆☆☆

NAME

ROASTERY	BREW METHOD
GRIND	EXTRAS
ORIGIN	SAMPLED

SERVING TYPE

CASUAL	ESPRESSO	CAPPUCCINO	LATTE	MOCHA	MACCHIATO	OTHER
☐	☐	☐	☐	☐	☐	☐

COLOR

LIGHT ⬤⬤⬤⬤ DARK

ADDITIONAL NOTES

FLAVOR WHEEL

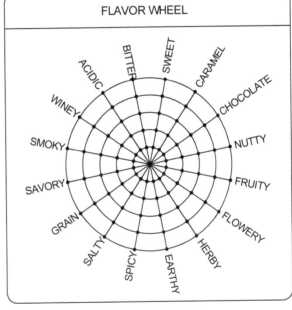

BITTER · SWEET · CARAMEL · CHOCOLATE · NUTTY · FRUITY · FLOWERY · HERBY · EARTHY · SPICY · SALTY · GRAIN · SAVORY · SMOKY · WINEY · ACIDIC

FINAL RATING

APPEARANCE	☆☆☆☆☆
AROMA	☆☆☆☆☆
TASTE	☆☆☆☆☆
CREMA	☆☆☆☆☆
OVERALL RATING	☆☆☆☆☆

🌰 NAME	
🏭 ROASTERY	☕ BREW METHOD
⚙️ GRIND	🧁 EXTRAS
🌍 ORIGIN	📅 SAMPLED

SERVING TYPE

CASUAL	ESPRESSO	CAPPUCCINO	LATTE	MOCHA	MACCHIATO	OTHER
☕	☕	☕	☕	☕	☕	☕
☐	☐	☐	☐	☐	☐	☐

COLOR

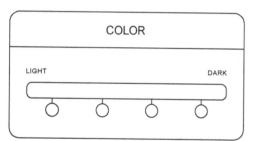

LIGHT   DARK

ADDITIONAL NOTES

FLAVOR WHEEL

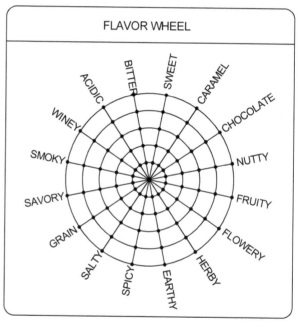

ACIDIC · BITTER · SWEET · CARAMEL · CHOCOLATE · NUTTY · FRUITY · FLOWERY · HERBY · EARTHY · SPICY · SALTY · GRAIN · SAVORY · SMOKY · WINEY

FINAL RATING

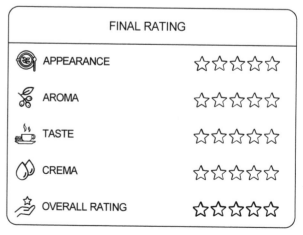

APPEARANCE	☆☆☆☆☆
AROMA	☆☆☆☆☆
TASTE	☆☆☆☆☆
CREMA	☆☆☆☆☆
OVERALL RATING	☆☆☆☆☆

NAME

ROASTERY	BREW METHOD
GRIND	EXTRAS
ORIGIN	SAMPLED

SERVING TYPE

CASUAL	ESPRESSO	CAPPUCCINO	LATTE	MOCHA	MACCHIATO	OTHER
☐	☐	☐	☐	☐	☐	☐

COLOR

LIGHT — DARK

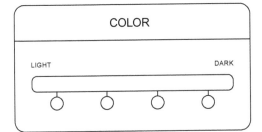

FLAVOR WHEEL

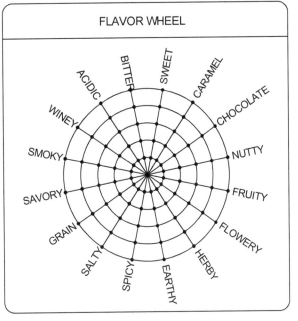

ACIDIC · BITTER · SWEET · CARAMEL · CHOCOLATE · NUTTY · FRUITY · FLOWERY · HERBY · EARTHY · SPICY · SALTY · GRAIN · SAVORY · SMOKY · WINEY

ADDITIONAL NOTES

FINAL RATING

APPEARANCE	☆☆☆☆☆
AROMA	☆☆☆☆☆
TASTE	☆☆☆☆☆
CREMA	☆☆☆☆☆
OVERALL RATING	☆☆☆☆☆

NAME

ROASTERY	BREW METHOD
GRIND	EXTRAS
ORIGIN	SAMPLED

SERVING TYPE

CASUAL	ESPRESSO	CAPPUCCINO	LATTE	MOCHA	MACCHIATO	OTHER
☐	☐	☐	☐	☐	☐	☐

COLOR

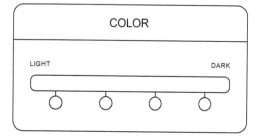

LIGHT   DARK

ADDITIONAL NOTES

FLAVOR WHEEL

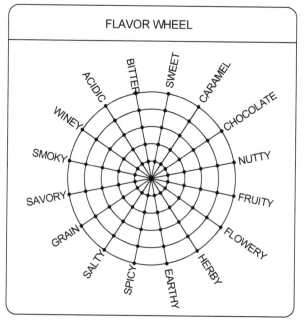

ACIDIC · BITTER · SWEET · CARAMEL · CHOCOLATE · NUTTY · FRUITY · FLOWERY · HERBY · EARTHY · SPICY · SALTY · GRAIN · SAVORY · SMOKY · WINEY

FINAL RATING

APPEARANCE	☆☆☆☆☆
AROMA	☆☆☆☆☆
TASTE	☆☆☆☆☆
CREMA	☆☆☆☆☆
OVERALL RATING	☆☆☆☆☆

NAME

ROASTERY	BREW METHOD
GRIND	EXTRAS
ORIGIN	SAMPLED

SERVING TYPE

CASUAL	ESPRESSO	CAPPUCCINO	LATTE	MOCHA	MACCHIATO	OTHER
☐	☐	☐	☐	☐	☐	☐

COLOR

LIGHT　　　　　　　　　　　DARK

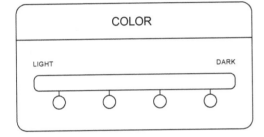

ADDITIONAL NOTES

FLAVOR WHEEL

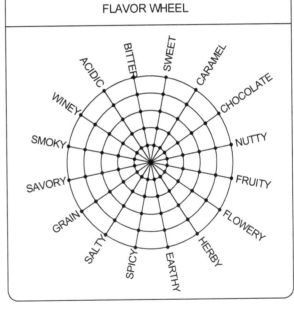

BITTER · SWEET · CARAMEL · CHOCOLATE · NUTTY · FRUITY · FLOWERY · HERBY · EARTHY · SPICY · SALTY · GRAIN · SAVORY · SMOKY · WINEY · ACIDIC

FINAL RATING

APPEARANCE	☆☆☆☆☆
AROMA	☆☆☆☆☆
TASTE	☆☆☆☆☆
CREMA	☆☆☆☆☆
OVERALL RATING	☆☆☆☆☆

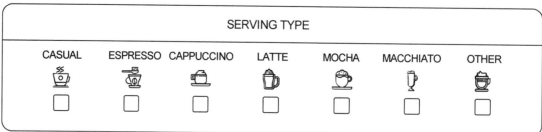 NAME	
ROASTERY	BREW METHOD
GRIND	EXTRAS
ORIGIN	SAMPLED

SERVING TYPE

CASUAL	ESPRESSO	CAPPUCCINO	LATTE	MOCHA	MACCHIATO	OTHER
☐	☐	☐	☐	☐	☐	☐

COLOR

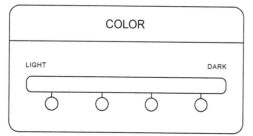

LIGHT   DARK

FLAVOR WHEEL

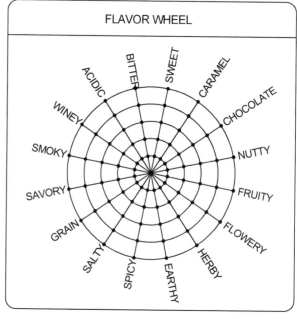

ACIDIC · BITTER · SWEET · CARAMEL · CHOCOLATE · NUTTY · FRUITY · FLOWERY · HERBY · EARTHY · SPICY · SALTY · GRAIN · SAVORY · SMOKY · WINEY

ADDITIONAL NOTES

FINAL RATING

APPEARANCE	☆☆☆☆☆
AROMA	☆☆☆☆☆
TASTE	☆☆☆☆☆
CREMA	☆☆☆☆☆
OVERALL RATING	☆☆☆☆☆

NAME	
ROASTERY	BREW METHOD
GRIND	EXTRAS
ORIGIN	SAMPLED

SERVING TYPE

CASUAL	ESPRESSO	CAPPUCCINO	LATTE	MOCHA	MACCHIATO	OTHER
☐	☐	☐	☐	☐	☐	☐

COLOR

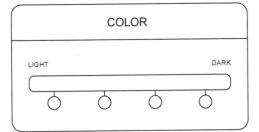

LIGHT   DARK

FLAVOR WHEEL

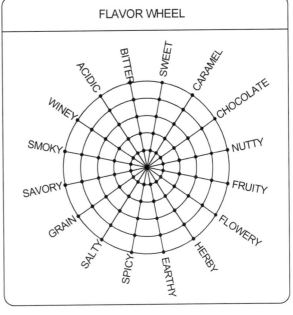

ACIDIC · BITTER · SWEET · CARAMEL · CHOCOLATE · NUTTY · FRUITY · FLOWERY · HERBY · EARTHY · SPICY · SALTY · GRAIN · SAVORY · SMOKY · WINEY

ADDITIONAL NOTES

FINAL RATING

APPEARANCE	☆☆☆☆☆
AROMA	☆☆☆☆☆
TASTE	☆☆☆☆☆
CREMA	☆☆☆☆☆
OVERALL RATING	☆☆☆☆☆

NAME

ROASTERY	BREW METHOD
GRIND	EXTRAS
ORIGIN	SAMPLED

SERVING TYPE

CASUAL	ESPRESSO	CAPPUCCINO	LATTE	MOCHA	MACCHIATO	OTHER
☐	☐	☐	☐	☐	☐	☐

COLOR

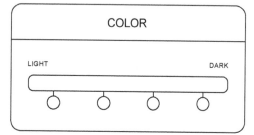

LIGHT — DARK

FLAVOR WHEEL

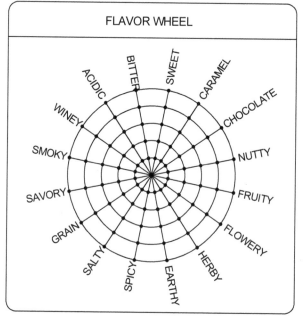

ADDITIONAL NOTES

FINAL RATING

APPEARANCE	☆☆☆☆☆
AROMA	☆☆☆☆☆
TASTE	☆☆☆☆☆
CREMA	☆☆☆☆☆
OVERALL RATING	☆☆☆☆☆

NAME

ROASTERY	BREW METHOD
GRIND	EXTRAS
ORIGIN	SAMPLED

SERVING TYPE

CASUAL	ESPRESSO	CAPPUCCINO	LATTE	MOCHA	MACCHIATO	OTHER
☐	☐	☐	☐	☐	☐	☐

COLOR

LIGHT   DARK

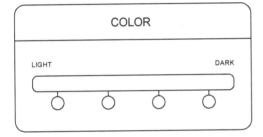

ADDITIONAL NOTES

FLAVOR WHEEL

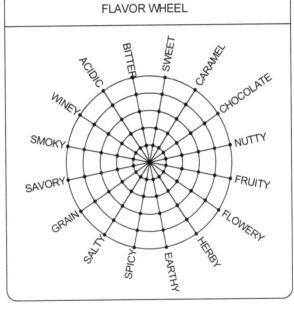

ACIDIC · BITTER · SWEET · CARAMEL · CHOCOLATE · NUTTY · FRUITY · FLOWERY · HERBY · EARTHY · SPICY · SALTY · GRAIN · SAVORY · SMOKY · WINEY

FINAL RATING

APPEARANCE	☆☆☆☆☆
AROMA	☆☆☆☆☆
TASTE	☆☆☆☆☆
CREMA	☆☆☆☆☆
OVERALL RATING	☆☆☆☆☆

🫘 NAME	
🏭 ROASTERY	☕ BREW METHOD
⚙️ GRIND	🧁 EXTRAS
🌍 ORIGIN	📅 SAMPLED

SERVING TYPE

CASUAL	ESPRESSO	CAPPUCCINO	LATTE	MOCHA	MACCHIATO	OTHER
☐	☐	☐	☐	☐	☐	☐

COLOR

LIGHT ———————— DARK

○   ○   ○   ○

ADDITIONAL NOTES

FLAVOR WHEEL

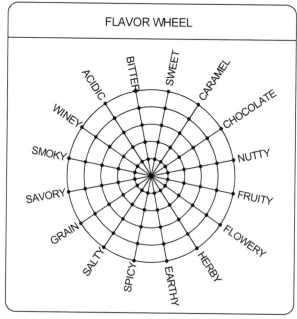

ACIDIC · BITTER · SWEET · CARAMEL · CHOCOLATE · NUTTY · FRUITY · FLOWERY · HERBY · EARTHY · SPICY · SALTY · GRAIN · SAVORY · SMOKY · WINEY

FINAL RATING

🏵️ APPEARANCE	☆☆☆☆☆
🌿 AROMA	☆☆☆☆☆
☕ TASTE	☆☆☆☆☆
💧 CREMA	☆☆☆☆☆
🖐️ OVERALL RATING	☆☆☆☆☆

NAME

ROASTERY	BREW METHOD
GRIND	EXTRAS
ORIGIN	SAMPLED

SERVING TYPE

CASUAL	ESPRESSO	CAPPUCCINO	LATTE	MOCHA	MACCHIATO	OTHER
☐	☐	☐	☐	☐	☐	☐

COLOR

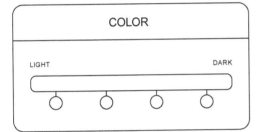

LIGHT — DARK

FLAVOR WHEEL

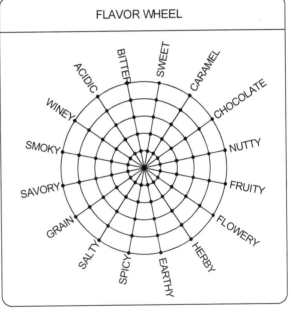

BITTER · SWEET · CARAMEL · CHOCOLATE · NUTTY · FRUITY · FLOWERY · HERBY · EARTHY · SPICY · SALTY · GRAIN · SAVORY · SMOKY · WINEY · ACIDIC

ADDITIONAL NOTES

FINAL RATING

APPEARANCE		☆☆☆☆☆
AROMA		☆☆☆☆☆
TASTE		☆☆☆☆☆
CREMA		☆☆☆☆☆
OVERALL RATING		☆☆☆☆☆

NAME

ROASTERY	BREW METHOD
GRIND	EXTRAS
ORIGIN	SAMPLED

SERVING TYPE

CASUAL	ESPRESSO	CAPPUCCINO	LATTE	MOCHA	MACCHIATO	OTHER
☐	☐	☐	☐	☐	☐	☐

COLOR

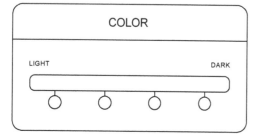

LIGHT · · · · DARK

FLAVOR WHEEL

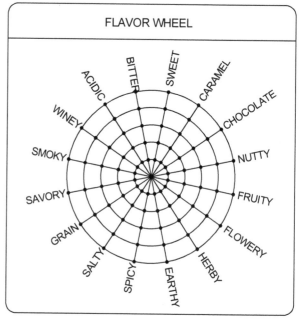

ACIDIC · BITTER · SWEET · CARAMEL · CHOCOLATE · NUTTY · FRUITY · FLOWERY · HERBY · EARTHY · SPICY · SALTY · GRAIN · SAVORY · SMOKY · WINEY

ADDITIONAL NOTES

FINAL RATING

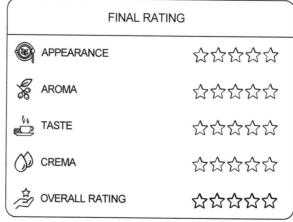

APPEARANCE	☆☆☆☆☆
AROMA	☆☆☆☆☆
TASTE	☆☆☆☆☆
CREMA	☆☆☆☆☆
OVERALL RATING	☆☆☆☆☆

NAME

ROASTERY	BREW METHOD
GRIND	EXTRAS
ORIGIN	SAMPLED

SERVING TYPE

CASUAL	ESPRESSO	CAPPUCCINO	LATTE	MOCHA	MACCHIATO	OTHER
☐	☐	☐	☐	☐	☐	☐

COLOR

LIGHT   DARK

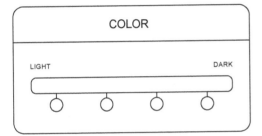

ADDITIONAL NOTES

FLAVOR WHEEL

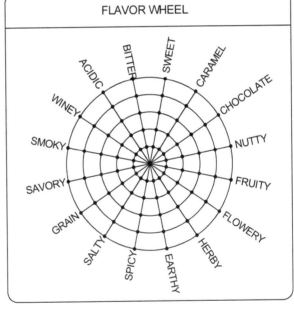

FINAL RATING

APPEARANCE	☆☆☆☆☆
AROMA	☆☆☆☆☆
TASTE	☆☆☆☆☆
CREMA	☆☆☆☆☆
OVERALL RATING	☆☆☆☆☆

🫘 NAME	
🎒 ROASTERY	🖨️ BREW METHOD
⚙️ GRIND	🧁 EXTRAS
🌐 ORIGIN	📅 SAMPLED

SERVING TYPE

CASUAL	ESPRESSO	CAPPUCCINO	LATTE	MOCHA	MACCHIATO	OTHER
☐	☐	☐	☐	☐	☐	☐

COLOR

LIGHT   DARK

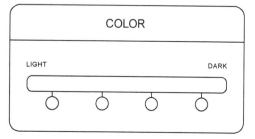

ADDITIONAL NOTES

FLAVOR WHEEL

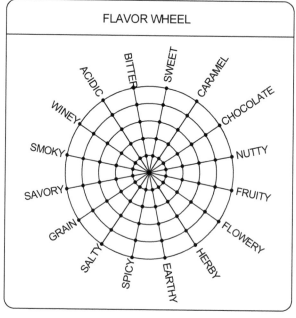

FINAL RATING

🎯 APPEARANCE	☆☆☆☆☆
🌿 AROMA	☆☆☆☆☆
☕ TASTE	☆☆☆☆☆
💧 CREMA	☆☆☆☆☆
🖐️ OVERALL RATING	☆☆☆☆☆

NAME

ROASTERY	BREW METHOD
GRIND	EXTRAS
ORIGIN	SAMPLED

SERVING TYPE

CASUAL	ESPRESSO	CAPPUCCINO	LATTE	MOCHA	MACCHIATO	OTHER
☐	☐	☐	☐	☐	☐	☐

COLOR

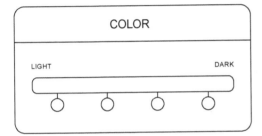

LIGHT   DARK

FLAVOR WHEEL

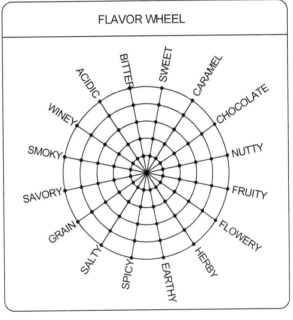

ADDITIONAL NOTES

FINAL RATING

APPEARANCE	☆☆☆☆☆
AROMA	☆☆☆☆☆
TASTE	☆☆☆☆☆
CREMA	☆☆☆☆☆
OVERALL RATING	☆☆☆☆☆

🫘 NAME	
🗄 ROASTERY	☕ BREW METHOD
⚙ GRIND	🧁 EXTRAS
🌍 ORIGIN	📅 SAMPLED

SERVING TYPE

CASUAL	ESPRESSO	CAPPUCCINO	LATTE	MOCHA	MACCHIATO	OTHER
☕	☕	☕	🥤	☕	🥛	🥤
☐	☐	☐	☐	☐	☐	☐

COLOR

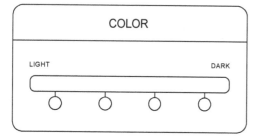

LIGHT   DARK

FLAVOR WHEEL

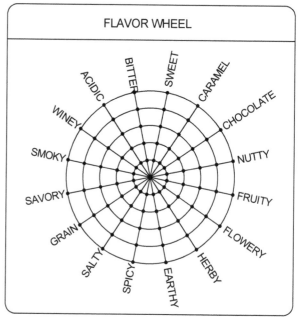

ADDITIONAL NOTES

FINAL RATING

🍩 APPEARANCE	☆☆☆☆☆
🌿 AROMA	☆☆☆☆☆
☕ TASTE	☆☆☆☆☆
💧 CREMA	☆☆☆☆☆
🏅 OVERALL RATING	☆☆☆☆☆

NAME

ROASTERY	BREW METHOD
GRIND	EXTRAS
ORIGIN	SAMPLED

SERVING TYPE

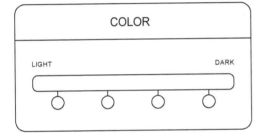

CASUAL	ESPRESSO	CAPPUCCINO	LATTE	MOCHA	MACCHIATO	OTHER
☐	☐	☐	☐	☐	☐	☐

COLOR

LIGHT　　　　　　　　　　DARK

FLAVOR WHEEL

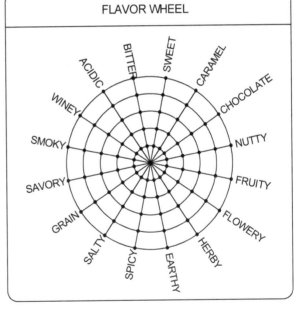

ADDITIONAL NOTES

FINAL RATING

APPEARANCE	☆☆☆☆☆
AROMA	☆☆☆☆☆
TASTE	☆☆☆☆☆
CREMA	☆☆☆☆☆
OVERALL RATING	☆☆☆☆☆

NAME

ROASTERY	BREW METHOD
GRIND	EXTRAS
ORIGIN	SAMPLED

SERVING TYPE

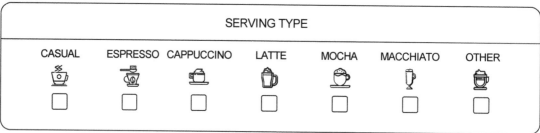

CASUAL	ESPRESSO	CAPPUCCINO	LATTE	MOCHA	MACCHIATO	OTHER
☐	☐	☐	☐	☐	☐	☐

COLOR

LIGHT   DARK

ADDITIONAL NOTES

FLAVOR WHEEL

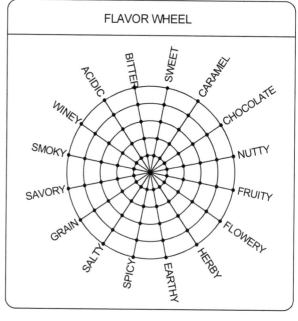

FINAL RATING

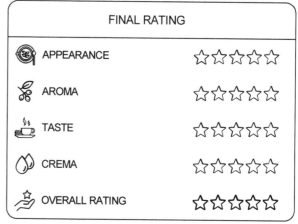

APPEARANCE	☆☆☆☆☆
AROMA	☆☆☆☆☆
TASTE	☆☆☆☆☆
CREMA	☆☆☆☆☆
OVERALL RATING	☆☆☆☆☆

NAME

ROASTERY	BREW METHOD
GRIND	EXTRAS
ORIGIN	SAMPLED

SERVING TYPE

CASUAL	ESPRESSO	CAPPUCCINO	LATTE	MOCHA	MACCHIATO	OTHER
☐	☐	☐	☐	☐	☐	☐

COLOR

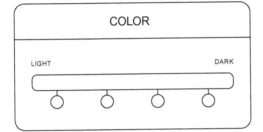

LIGHT   DARK

FLAVOR WHEEL

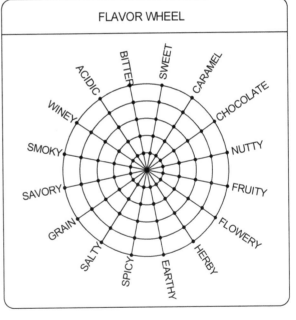

ADDITIONAL NOTES

FINAL RATING

APPEARANCE	☆☆☆☆☆
AROMA	☆☆☆☆☆
TASTE	☆☆☆☆☆
CREMA	☆☆☆☆☆
OVERALL RATING	☆☆☆☆☆

NAME

ROASTERY	BREW METHOD
GRIND	EXTRAS
ORIGIN	SAMPLED

SERVING TYPE

CASUAL	ESPRESSO	CAPPUCCINO	LATTE	MOCHA	MACCHIATO	OTHER
☐	☐	☐	☐	☐	☐	☐

COLOR

LIGHT — DARK

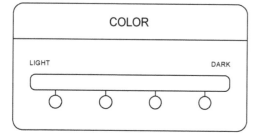

FLAVOR WHEEL

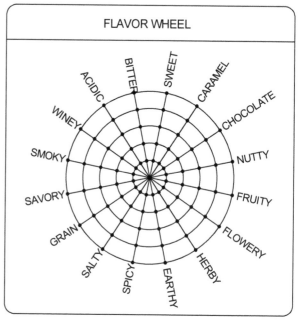

ACIDIC, BITTER, SWEET, CARAMEL, CHOCOLATE, NUTTY, FRUITY, FLOWERY, HERBY, EARTHY, SPICY, SALTY, GRAIN, SAVORY, SMOKY, WINEY

ADDITIONAL NOTES

FINAL RATING

APPEARANCE	☆☆☆☆☆
AROMA	☆☆☆☆☆
TASTE	☆☆☆☆☆
CREMA	☆☆☆☆☆
OVERALL RATING	☆☆☆☆☆

NAME

ROASTERY	BREW METHOD
GRIND	EXTRAS
ORIGIN	SAMPLED

SERVING TYPE

CASUAL	ESPRESSO	CAPPUCCINO	LATTE	MOCHA	MACCHIATO	OTHER
☐	☐	☐	☐	☐	☐	☐

COLOR

LIGHT   DARK

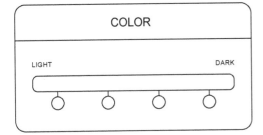

FLAVOR WHEEL

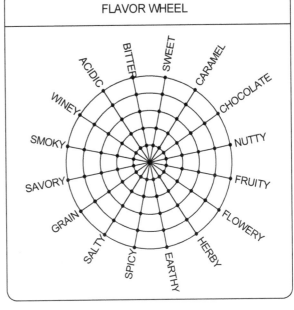

BITTER · SWEET · CARAMEL · CHOCOLATE · NUTTY · FRUITY · FLOWERY · HERBY · EARTHY · SPICY · SALTY · GRAIN · SAVORY · SMOKY · WINEY · ACIDIC

ADDITIONAL NOTES

FINAL RATING

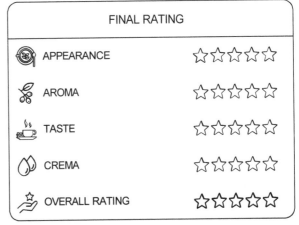

APPEARANCE	☆☆☆☆☆
AROMA	☆☆☆☆☆
TASTE	☆☆☆☆☆
CREMA	☆☆☆☆☆
OVERALL RATING	☆☆☆☆☆

NAME

ROASTERY	BREW METHOD
GRIND	EXTRAS
ORIGIN	SAMPLED

SERVING TYPE

CASUAL	ESPRESSO	CAPPUCCINO	LATTE	MOCHA	MACCHIATO	OTHER
☐	☐	☐	☐	☐	☐	☐

COLOR

LIGHT   DARK

FLAVOR WHEEL

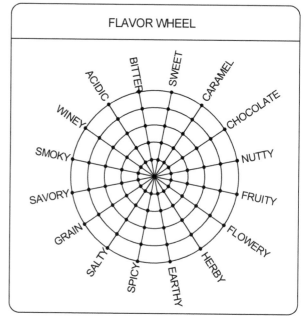

ADDITIONAL NOTES

FINAL RATING

APPEARANCE	☆☆☆☆☆
AROMA	☆☆☆☆☆
TASTE	☆☆☆☆☆
CREMA	☆☆☆☆☆
OVERALL RATING	☆☆☆☆☆

NAME

ROASTERY	BREW METHOD
GRIND	EXTRAS
ORIGIN	SAMPLED

SERVING TYPE

CASUAL	ESPRESSO	CAPPUCCINO	LATTE	MOCHA	MACCHIATO	OTHER
☐	☐	☐	☐	☐	☐	☐

COLOR

LIGHT   DARK

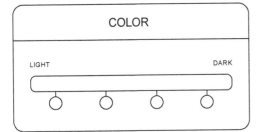

ADDITIONAL NOTES

FLAVOR WHEEL

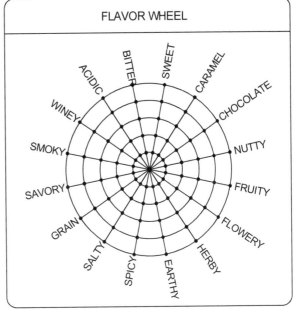

FINAL RATING

APPEARANCE	☆☆☆☆☆
AROMA	☆☆☆☆☆
TASTE	☆☆☆☆☆
CREMA	☆☆☆☆☆
OVERALL RATING	☆☆☆☆☆

NAME

ROASTERY	BREW METHOD
GRIND	EXTRAS
ORIGIN	SAMPLED

SERVING TYPE

CASUAL	ESPRESSO	CAPPUCCINO	LATTE	MOCHA	MACCHIATO	OTHER
☐	☐	☐	☐	☐	☐	☐

COLOR

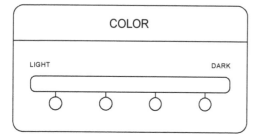

LIGHT   DARK

ADDITIONAL NOTES

FLAVOR WHEEL

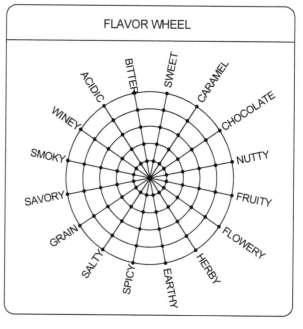

ACIDIC · BITTER · SWEET · CARAMEL · CHOCOLATE · NUTTY · FRUITY · FLOWERY · HERBY · EARTHY · SPICY · SALTY · GRAIN · SAVORY · SMOKY · WINEY

FINAL RATING

APPEARANCE		☆☆☆☆☆
AROMA		☆☆☆☆☆
TASTE		☆☆☆☆☆
CREMA		☆☆☆☆☆
OVERALL RATING		☆☆☆☆☆

NAME

ROASTERY	BREW METHOD
GRIND	EXTRAS
ORIGIN	SAMPLED

SERVING TYPE

CASUAL	ESPRESSO	CAPPUCCINO	LATTE	MOCHA	MACCHIATO	OTHER
☐	☐	☐	☐	☐	☐	☐

COLOR

LIGHT   DARK

FLAVOR WHEEL

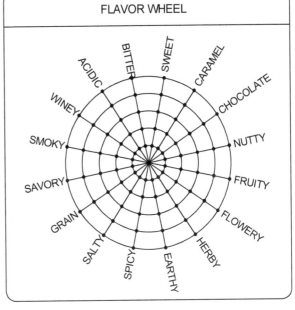

BITTER, SWEET, CARAMEL, CHOCOLATE, NUTTY, FRUITY, FLOWERY, HERBY, EARTHY, SPICY, SALTY, GRAIN, SAVORY, SMOKY, WINEY, ACIDIC

ADDITIONAL NOTES

FINAL RATING

APPEARANCE	☆☆☆☆☆
AROMA	☆☆☆☆☆
TASTE	☆☆☆☆☆
CREMA	☆☆☆☆☆
OVERALL RATING	☆☆☆☆☆

NAME	
ROASTERY	BREW METHOD
GRIND	EXTRAS
ORIGIN	SAMPLED

SERVING TYPE

CASUAL	ESPRESSO	CAPPUCCINO	LATTE	MOCHA	MACCHIATO	OTHER
☐	☐	☐	☐	☐	☐	☐

COLOR

LIGHT   DARK

FLAVOR WHEEL

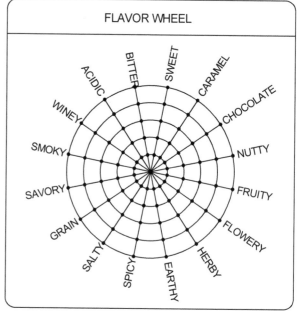

ACIDIC · BITTER · SWEET · CARAMEL · CHOCOLATE · NUTTY · FRUITY · FLOWERY · HERBY · EARTHY · SPICY · SALTY · GRAIN · SAVORY · SMOKY · WINEY

ADDITIONAL NOTES

FINAL RATING

APPEARANCE	☆☆☆☆☆
AROMA	☆☆☆☆☆
TASTE	☆☆☆☆☆
CREMA	☆☆☆☆☆
OVERALL RATING	☆☆☆☆☆

NAME

ROASTERY	BREW METHOD
GRIND	EXTRAS
ORIGIN	SAMPLED

SERVING TYPE

CASUAL	ESPRESSO	CAPPUCCINO	LATTE	MOCHA	MACCHIATO	OTHER
☐	☐	☐	☐	☐	☐	☐

COLOR

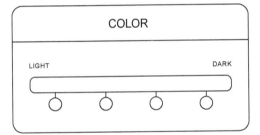

LIGHT   DARK

FLAVOR WHEEL

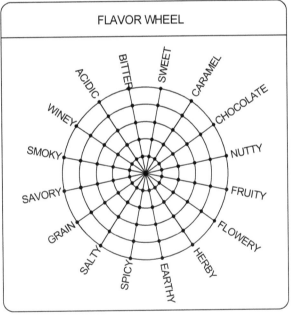

ADDITIONAL NOTES

FINAL RATING

APPEARANCE	☆☆☆☆☆
AROMA	☆☆☆☆☆
TASTE	☆☆☆☆☆
CREMA	☆☆☆☆☆
OVERALL RATING	☆☆☆☆☆

NAME

ROASTERY	BREW METHOD
GRIND	EXTRAS
ORIGIN	SAMPLED

SERVING TYPE

CASUAL	ESPRESSO	CAPPUCCINO	LATTE	MOCHA	MACCHIATO	OTHER
☐	☐	☐	☐	☐	☐	☐

COLOR

LIGHT   DARK

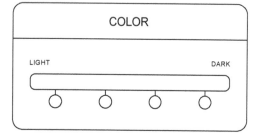

FLAVOR WHEEL

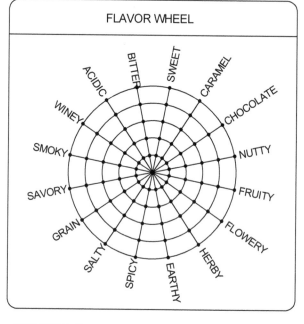

BITTER · SWEET · CARAMEL · CHOCOLATE · NUTTY · FRUITY · FLOWERY · HERBY · EARTHY · SPICY · SALTY · GRAIN · SAVORY · SMOKY · WINEY · ACIDIC

ADDITIONAL NOTES

FINAL RATING

APPEARANCE	☆☆☆☆☆
AROMA	☆☆☆☆☆
TASTE	☆☆☆☆☆
CREMA	☆☆☆☆☆
OVERALL RATING	☆☆☆☆☆

NAME

ROASTERY	BREW METHOD
GRIND	EXTRAS
ORIGIN	SAMPLED

SERVING TYPE

CASUAL	ESPRESSO	CAPPUCCINO	LATTE	MOCHA	MACCHIATO	OTHER
☐	☐	☐	☐	☐	☐	☐

COLOR

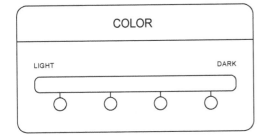

LIGHT   DARK

FLAVOR WHEEL

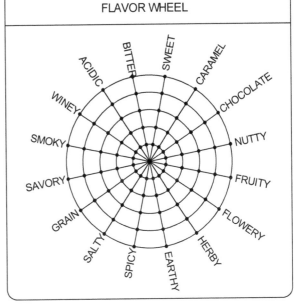

BITTER · SWEET · CARAMEL · ACIDIC · CHOCOLATE · WINEY · NUTTY · SMOKY · FRUITY · SAVORY · FLOWERY · GRAIN · HERBY · SALTY · SPICY · EARTHY

ADDITIONAL NOTES

FINAL RATING

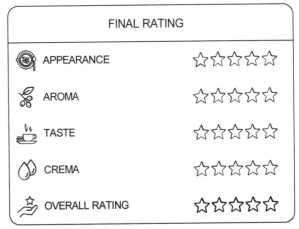

APPEARANCE	☆☆☆☆☆
AROMA	☆☆☆☆☆
TASTE	☆☆☆☆☆
CREMA	☆☆☆☆☆
OVERALL RATING	☆☆☆☆☆

🫘 NAME	
🖥️ ROASTERY	☕ BREW METHOD
⚙️ GRIND	🧁 EXTRAS
🌍 ORIGIN	📅 SAMPLED

SERVING TYPE

CASUAL	ESPRESSO	CAPPUCCINO	LATTE	MOCHA	MACCHIATO	OTHER
☐	☐	☐	☐	☐	☐	☐

COLOR

LIGHT   DARK

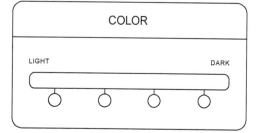

FLAVOR WHEEL

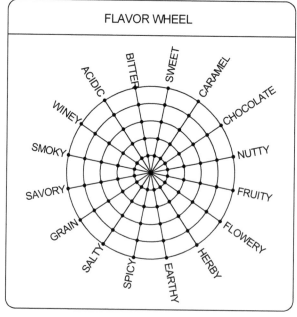

ADDITIONAL NOTES

FINAL RATING

🌀 APPEARANCE	☆☆☆☆☆
🌿 AROMA	☆☆☆☆☆
☕ TASTE	☆☆☆☆☆
💧 CREMA	☆☆☆☆☆
🖐️ OVERALL RATING	☆☆☆☆☆

NAME

ROASTERY	BREW METHOD
GRIND	EXTRAS
ORIGIN	SAMPLED

SERVING TYPE

CASUAL	ESPRESSO	CAPPUCCINO	LATTE	MOCHA	MACCHIATO	OTHER
☐	☐	☐	☐	☐	☐	☐

COLOR

LIGHT   DARK

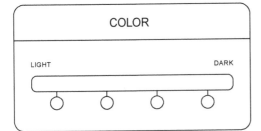

FLAVOR WHEEL

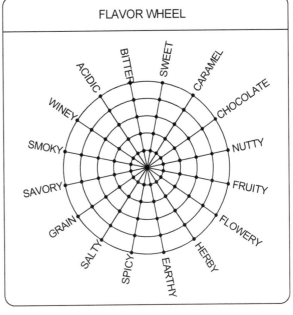

ADDITIONAL NOTES

FINAL RATING

APPEARANCE	☆☆☆☆☆
AROMA	☆☆☆☆☆
TASTE	☆☆☆☆☆
CREMA	☆☆☆☆☆
OVERALL RATING	☆☆☆☆☆

◊ NAME	
▦ ROASTERY	☕ BREW METHOD
⚙ GRIND	🧁 EXTRAS
🌐 ORIGIN	📅 SAMPLED

SERVING TYPE

CASUAL	ESPRESSO	CAPPUCCINO	LATTE	MOCHA	MACCHIATO	OTHER
☐	☐	☐	☐	☐	☐	☐

COLOR

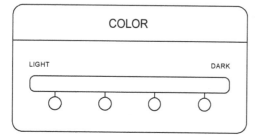

LIGHT   DARK

FLAVOR WHEEL

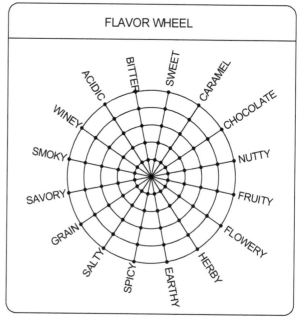

ADDITIONAL NOTES

FINAL RATING

🎯 APPEARANCE	☆☆☆☆☆
🌿 AROMA	☆☆☆☆☆
☕ TASTE	☆☆☆☆☆
💧 CREMA	☆☆☆☆☆
✋ OVERALL RATING	☆☆☆☆☆

NAME

ROASTERY	BREW METHOD
GRIND	EXTRAS
ORIGIN	SAMPLED

SERVING TYPE

CASUAL	ESPRESSO	CAPPUCCINO	LATTE	MOCHA	MACCHIATO	OTHER
☐	☐	☐	☐	☐	☐	☐

COLOR

LIGHT   DARK

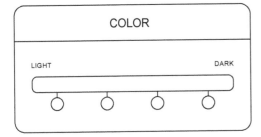

FLAVOR WHEEL

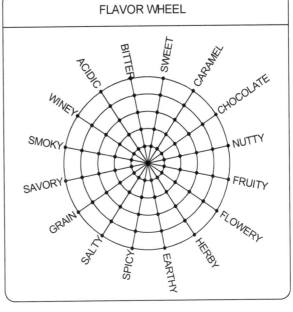

BITTER, SWEET, CARAMEL, CHOCOLATE, NUTTY, FRUITY, FLOWERY, HERBY, EARTHY, SPICY, SALTY, GRAIN, SAVORY, SMOKY, WINEY, ACIDIC

ADDITIONAL NOTES

FINAL RATING

APPEARANCE	☆☆☆☆☆
AROMA	☆☆☆☆☆
TASTE	☆☆☆☆☆
CREMA	☆☆☆☆☆
OVERALL RATING	☆☆☆☆☆

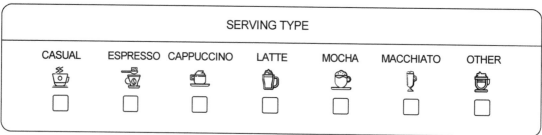 NAME	
ROASTERY	BREW METHOD
GRIND	EXTRAS
ORIGIN	SAMPLED

SERVING TYPE

CASUAL	ESPRESSO	CAPPUCCINO	LATTE	MOCHA	MACCHIATO	OTHER
☐	☐	☐	☐	☐	☐	☐

COLOR

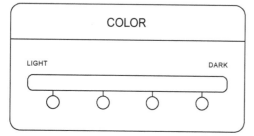

LIGHT ———————————————— DARK

FLAVOR WHEEL

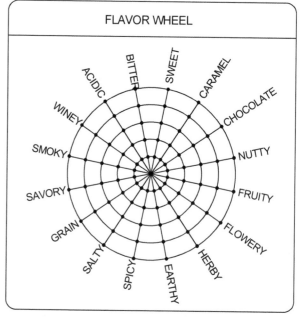

ACIDIC · BITTER · SWEET · CARAMEL · CHOCOLATE · NUTTY · FRUITY · FLOWERY · HERBY · EARTHY · SPICY · SALTY · GRAIN · SAVORY · SMOKY · WINEY

ADDITIONAL NOTES

FINAL RATING

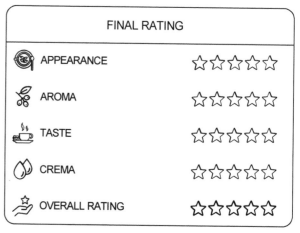

APPEARANCE	☆☆☆☆☆
AROMA	☆☆☆☆☆
TASTE	☆☆☆☆☆
CREMA	☆☆☆☆☆
OVERALL RATING	☆☆☆☆☆

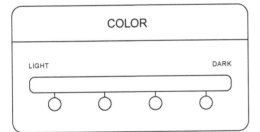 NAME	
ROASTERY	BREW METHOD
GRIND	EXTRAS
ORIGIN	SAMPLED

SERVING TYPE

CASUAL	ESPRESSO	CAPPUCCINO	LATTE	MOCHA	MACCHIATO	OTHER
☐	☐	☐	☐	☐	☐	☐

COLOR

LIGHT   DARK

ADDITIONAL NOTES

FLAVOR WHEEL

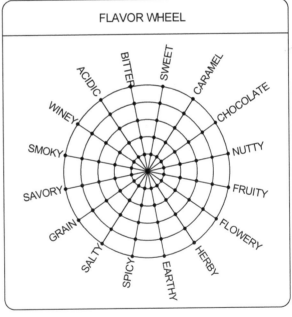

FINAL RATING

APPEARANCE	☆☆☆☆☆
AROMA	☆☆☆☆☆
TASTE	☆☆☆☆☆
CREMA	☆☆☆☆☆
OVERALL RATING	☆☆☆☆☆

NAME

ROASTERY	BREW METHOD
GRIND	EXTRAS
ORIGIN	SAMPLED

SERVING TYPE

CASUAL	ESPRESSO	CAPPUCCINO	LATTE	MOCHA	MACCHIATO	OTHER
☐	☐	☐	☐	☐	☐	☐

COLOR

LIGHT — DARK

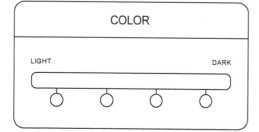

FLAVOR WHEEL

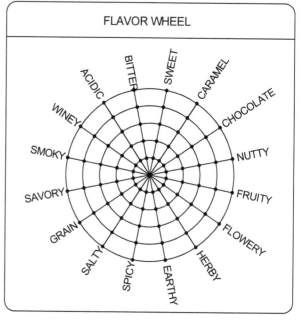

ADDITIONAL NOTES

FINAL RATING

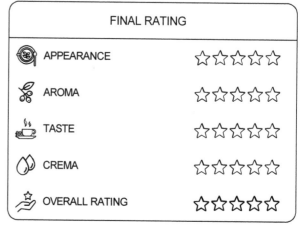

APPEARANCE	☆☆☆☆☆
AROMA	☆☆☆☆☆
TASTE	☆☆☆☆☆
CREMA	☆☆☆☆☆
OVERALL RATING	☆☆☆☆☆

NAME

ROASTERY	BREW METHOD
GRIND	EXTRAS
ORIGIN	SAMPLED

SERVING TYPE

CASUAL	ESPRESSO	CAPPUCCINO	LATTE	MOCHA	MACCHIATO	OTHER
☐	☐	☐	☐	☐	☐	☐

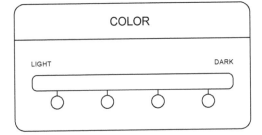

COLOR

LIGHT ——————————— DARK

ADDITIONAL NOTES

FLAVOR WHEEL

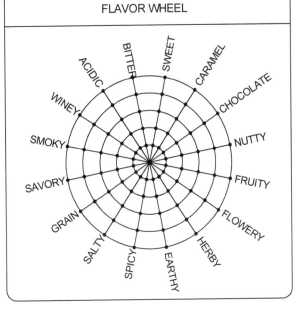

ACIDIC · BITTER · SWEET · CARAMEL · CHOCOLATE · NUTTY · FRUITY · FLOWERY · HERBY · EARTHY · SPICY · SALTY · GRAIN · SAVORY · SMOKY · WINEY

FINAL RATING

APPEARANCE	☆☆☆☆☆
AROMA	☆☆☆☆☆
TASTE	☆☆☆☆☆
CREMA	☆☆☆☆☆
OVERALL RATING	☆☆☆☆☆

NAME

ROASTERY	BREW METHOD
GRIND	EXTRAS
ORIGIN	SAMPLED

SERVING TYPE

CASUAL	ESPRESSO	CAPPUCCINO	LATTE	MOCHA	MACCHIATO	OTHER
☐	☐	☐	☐	☐	☐	☐

COLOR

LIGHT ———————————— DARK

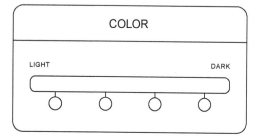

FLAVOR WHEEL

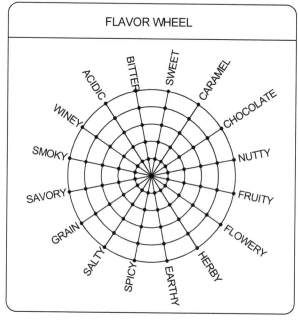

BITTER · SWEET · CARAMEL · CHOCOLATE · NUTTY · FRUITY · FLOWERY · HERBY · EARTHY · SPICY · SALTY · GRAIN · SAVORY · SMOKY · WINEY · ACIDIC

ADDITIONAL NOTES

FINAL RATING

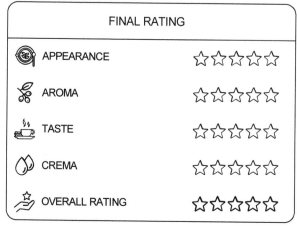

APPEARANCE	☆☆☆☆☆
AROMA	☆☆☆☆☆
TASTE	☆☆☆☆☆
CREMA	☆☆☆☆☆
OVERALL RATING	☆☆☆☆☆

NAME

ROASTERY	BREW METHOD
GRIND	EXTRAS
ORIGIN	SAMPLED

SERVING TYPE

CASUAL	ESPRESSO	CAPPUCCINO	LATTE	MOCHA	MACCHIATO	OTHER
☐	☐	☐	☐	☐	☐	☐

COLOR

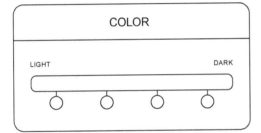

LIGHT   DARK

FLAVOR WHEEL

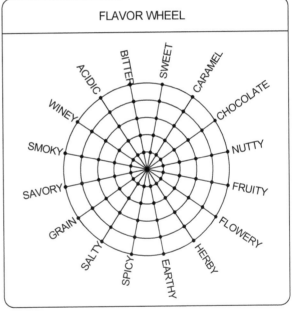

ACIDIC · BITTER · SWEET · CARAMEL · CHOCOLATE · NUTTY · FRUITY · FLOWERY · HERBY · EARTHY · SPICY · SALTY · GRAIN · SAVORY · SMOKY · WINEY

ADDITIONAL NOTES

FINAL RATING

APPEARANCE	☆☆☆☆☆
AROMA	☆☆☆☆☆
TASTE	☆☆☆☆☆
CREMA	☆☆☆☆☆
OVERALL RATING	☆☆☆☆☆

NAME

ROASTERY	BREW METHOD
GRIND	EXTRAS
ORIGIN	SAMPLED

SERVING TYPE

CASUAL	ESPRESSO	CAPPUCCINO	LATTE	MOCHA	MACCHIATO	OTHER
☐	☐	☐	☐	☐	☐	☐

COLOR

LIGHT   DARK

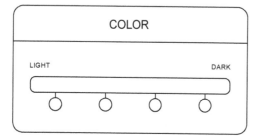

FLAVOR WHEEL

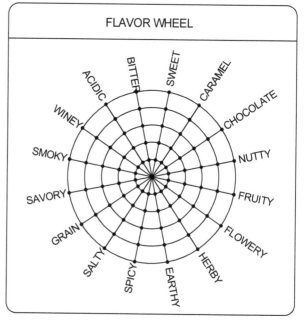

ADDITIONAL NOTES

FINAL RATING

APPEARANCE	☆☆☆☆☆
AROMA	☆☆☆☆☆
TASTE	☆☆☆☆☆
CREMA	☆☆☆☆☆
OVERALL RATING	☆☆☆☆☆

NAME

ROASTERY

BREW METHOD

GRIND

EXTRAS

ORIGIN

SAMPLED

SERVING TYPE

CASUAL	ESPRESSO	CAPPUCCINO	LATTE	MOCHA	MACCHIATO	OTHER
☐	☐	☐	☐	☐	☐	☐

COLOR

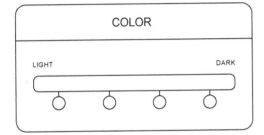

LIGHT   DARK

FLAVOR WHEEL

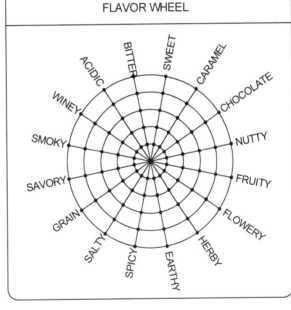

ADDITIONAL NOTES

FINAL RATING

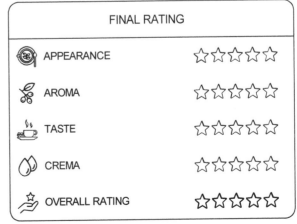

APPEARANCE ☆☆☆☆☆

AROMA ☆☆☆☆☆

TASTE ☆☆☆☆☆

CREMA ☆☆☆☆☆

OVERALL RATING ☆☆☆☆☆

NAME

ROASTERY	BREW METHOD
GRIND	EXTRAS
ORIGIN	SAMPLED

SERVING TYPE

CASUAL	ESPRESSO	CAPPUCCINO	LATTE	MOCHA	MACCHIATO	OTHER
☐	☐	☐	☐	☐	☐	☐

COLOR

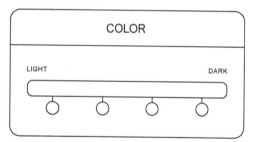

LIGHT — DARK

FLAVOR WHEEL

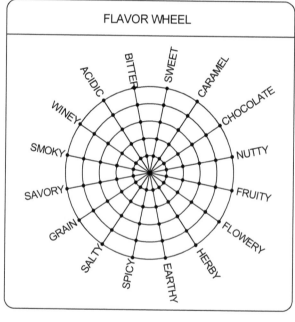

BITTER · SWEET · CARAMEL · CHOCOLATE · NUTTY · FRUITY · FLOWERY · HERBY · EARTHY · SPICY · SALTY · GRAIN · SAVORY · SMOKY · WINEY · ACIDIC

ADDITIONAL NOTES

FINAL RATING

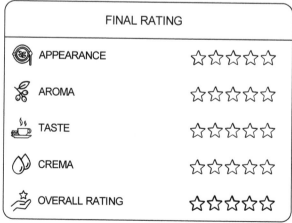

APPEARANCE	☆☆☆☆☆
AROMA	☆☆☆☆☆
TASTE	☆☆☆☆☆
CREMA	☆☆☆☆☆
OVERALL RATING	☆☆☆☆☆

🫘 NAME	
📇 ROASTERY	☕ BREW METHOD
⚙️ GRIND	🧁 EXTRAS
🌍 ORIGIN	📅 SAMPLED

SERVING TYPE

CASUAL	ESPRESSO	CAPPUCCINO	LATTE	MOCHA	MACCHIATO	OTHER
☕	☕	☕	☕	☕	☕	☕
☐	☐	☐	☐	☐	☐	☐

COLOR

LIGHT   DARK

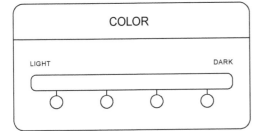

FLAVOR WHEEL

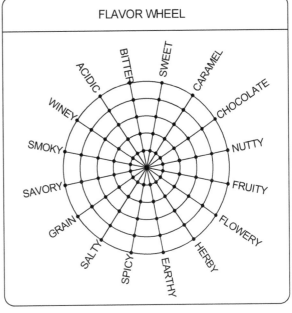

ADDITIONAL NOTES

FINAL RATING

🍩 APPEARANCE	☆☆☆☆☆
🌿 AROMA	☆☆☆☆☆
☕ TASTE	☆☆☆☆☆
💧 CREMA	☆☆☆☆☆
🖐️ OVERALL RATING	☆☆☆☆☆

NAME

ROASTERY	BREW METHOD
GRIND	EXTRAS
ORIGIN	SAMPLED

SERVING TYPE

CASUAL	ESPRESSO	CAPPUCCINO	LATTE	MOCHA	MACCHIATO	OTHER
☐	☐	☐	☐	☐	☐	☐

COLOR

LIGHT   DARK

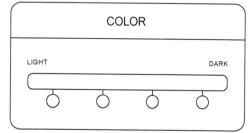

ADDITIONAL NOTES

FLAVOR WHEEL

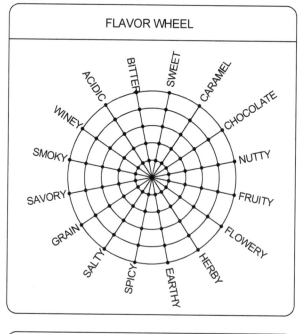

ACIDIC · BITTER · SWEET · CARAMEL · CHOCOLATE · NUTTY · FRUITY · FLOWERY · HERBY · EARTHY · SPICY · SALTY · GRAIN · SAVORY · SMOKY · WINEY

FINAL RATING

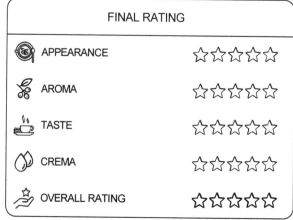

APPEARANCE	☆☆☆☆☆
AROMA	☆☆☆☆☆
TASTE	☆☆☆☆☆
CREMA	☆☆☆☆☆
OVERALL RATING	☆☆☆☆☆

NAME

ROASTERY	BREW METHOD
GRIND	EXTRAS
ORIGIN	SAMPLED

SERVING TYPE

CASUAL	ESPRESSO	CAPPUCCINO	LATTE	MOCHA	MACCHIATO	OTHER
☐	☐	☐	☐	☐	☐	☐

COLOR

LIGHT   DARK

○   ○   ○   ○

FLAVOR WHEEL

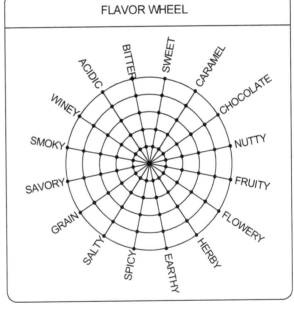

BITTER · SWEET · CARAMEL · ACIDIC · CHOCOLATE · WINEY · SMOKY · NUTTY · SAVORY · FRUITY · GRAIN · FLOWERY · SALTY · HERBY · SPICY · EARTHY

ADDITIONAL NOTES

FINAL RATING

APPEARANCE	☆☆☆☆☆
AROMA	☆☆☆☆☆
TASTE	☆☆☆☆☆
CREMA	☆☆☆☆☆
OVERALL RATING	☆☆☆☆☆

NAME

ROASTERY	BREW METHOD
GRIND	EXTRAS
ORIGIN	SAMPLED

SERVING TYPE

CASUAL	ESPRESSO	CAPPUCCINO	LATTE	MOCHA	MACCHIATO	OTHER
☐	☐	☐	☐	☐	☐	☐

COLOR

LIGHT   DARK

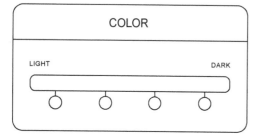

FLAVOR WHEEL

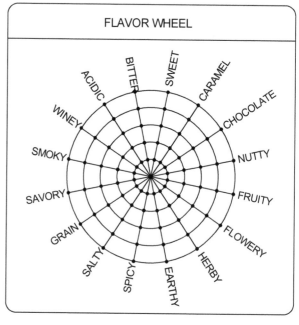

ADDITIONAL NOTES

FINAL RATING

APPEARANCE	☆☆☆☆☆
AROMA	☆☆☆☆☆
TASTE	☆☆☆☆☆
CREMA	☆☆☆☆☆
OVERALL RATING	☆☆☆☆☆

NAME

ROASTERY	BREW METHOD
GRIND	EXTRAS
ORIGIN	SAMPLED

SERVING TYPE

CASUAL	ESPRESSO	CAPPUCCINO	LATTE	MOCHA	MACCHIATO	OTHER
☐	☐	☐	☐	☐	☐	☐

COLOR

LIGHT   DARK

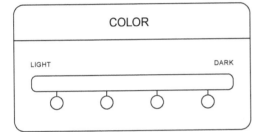

FLAVOR WHEEL

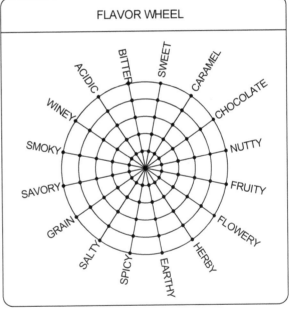

ADDITIONAL NOTES

FINAL RATING

APPEARANCE	☆☆☆☆☆
AROMA	☆☆☆☆☆
TASTE	☆☆☆☆☆
CREMA	☆☆☆☆☆
OVERALL RATING	☆☆☆☆☆

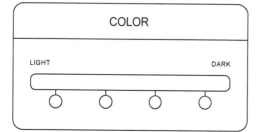 NAME	
🏷️ ROASTERY	☕ BREW METHOD
⚙️ GRIND	🧁 EXTRAS
🌍 ORIGIN	📅 SAMPLED

SERVING TYPE

CASUAL	ESPRESSO	CAPPUCCINO	LATTE	MOCHA	MACCHIATO	OTHER
☐	☐	☐	☐	☐	☐	☐

COLOR

LIGHT   DARK

FLAVOR WHEEL

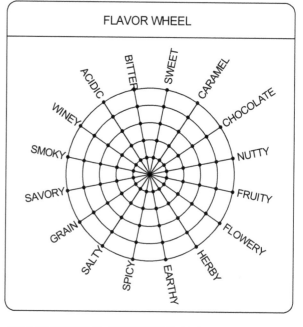

ACIDIC · BITTER · SWEET · CARAMEL · CHOCOLATE · NUTTY · FRUITY · FLOWERY · HERBY · EARTHY · SPICY · SALTY · GRAIN · SAVORY · SMOKY · WINEY

ADDITIONAL NOTES

FINAL RATING

🏵️ APPEARANCE		☆☆☆☆☆
🌿 AROMA		☆☆☆☆☆
☕ TASTE		☆☆☆☆☆
💧 CREMA		☆☆☆☆☆
✋ OVERALL RATING		☆☆☆☆☆

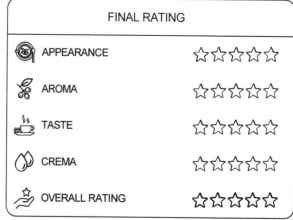

NAME

ROASTERY	BREW METHOD
GRIND	EXTRAS
ORIGIN	SAMPLED

SERVING TYPE

CASUAL	ESPRESSO	CAPPUCCINO	LATTE	MOCHA	MACCHIATO	OTHER
☐	☐	☐	☐	☐	☐	☐

COLOR

LIGHT   DARK

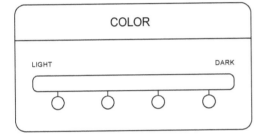

ADDITIONAL NOTES

FLAVOR WHEEL

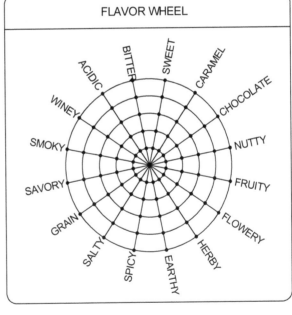

BITTER · SWEET · CARAMEL · CHOCOLATE · NUTTY · FRUITY · FLOWERY · HERBY · EARTHY · SPICY · SALTY · GRAIN · SAVORY · SMOKY · WINEY · ACIDIC

FINAL RATING

APPEARANCE	☆☆☆☆☆
AROMA	☆☆☆☆☆
TASTE	☆☆☆☆☆
CREMA	☆☆☆☆☆
OVERALL RATING	☆☆☆☆☆

NAME

ROASTERY	BREW METHOD
GRIND	EXTRAS
ORIGIN	SAMPLED

SERVING TYPE

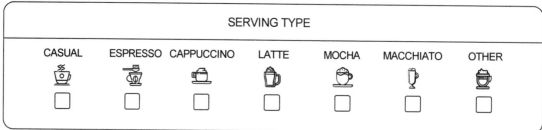

CASUAL	ESPRESSO	CAPPUCCINO	LATTE	MOCHA	MACCHIATO	OTHER
☐	☐	☐	☐	☐	☐	☐

COLOR

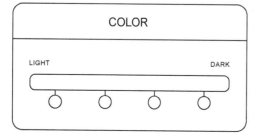

LIGHT   DARK

FLAVOR WHEEL

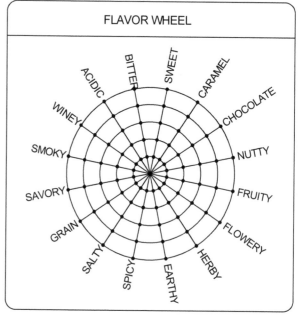

ADDITIONAL NOTES

FINAL RATING

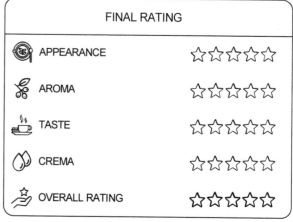

APPEARANCE	☆☆☆☆☆
AROMA	☆☆☆☆☆
TASTE	☆☆☆☆☆
CREMA	☆☆☆☆☆
OVERALL RATING	☆☆☆☆☆

NAME

ROASTERY	BREW METHOD
GRIND	EXTRAS
ORIGIN	SAMPLED

SERVING TYPE

CASUAL	ESPRESSO	CAPPUCCINO	LATTE	MOCHA	MACCHIATO	OTHER
☐	☐	☐	☐	☐	☐	☐

COLOR

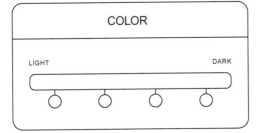

LIGHT — DARK

FLAVOR WHEEL

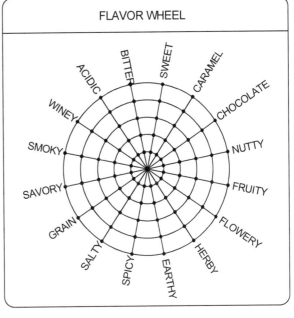

ACIDIC · BITTER · SWEET · CARAMEL · CHOCOLATE · NUTTY · FRUITY · FLOWERY · HERBY · EARTHY · SPICY · SALTY · GRAIN · SAVORY · SMOKY · WINEY

ADDITIONAL NOTES

FINAL RATING

APPEARANCE	☆☆☆☆☆
AROMA	☆☆☆☆☆
TASTE	☆☆☆☆☆
CREMA	☆☆☆☆☆
OVERALL RATING	☆☆☆☆☆

NAME

ROASTERY	BREW METHOD
GRIND	EXTRAS
ORIGIN	SAMPLED

SERVING TYPE

CASUAL	ESPRESSO	CAPPUCCINO	LATTE	MOCHA	MACCHIATO	OTHER
☐	☐	☐	☐	☐	☐	☐

COLOR

LIGHT   DARK

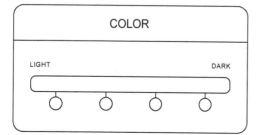

FLAVOR WHEEL

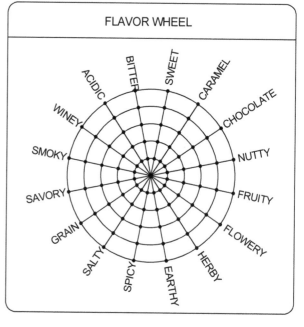

ADDITIONAL NOTES

FINAL RATING

APPEARANCE	☆☆☆☆☆
AROMA	☆☆☆☆☆
TASTE	☆☆☆☆☆
CREMA	☆☆☆☆☆
OVERALL RATING	☆☆☆☆☆

NAME

ROASTERY	BREW METHOD
GRIND	EXTRAS
ORIGIN	SAMPLED

SERVING TYPE

CASUAL	ESPRESSO	CAPPUCCINO	LATTE	MOCHA	MACCHIATO	OTHER
☐	☐	☐	☐	☐	☐	☐

COLOR

LIGHT   DARK

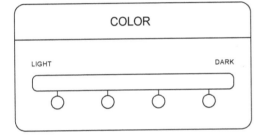

FLAVOR WHEEL

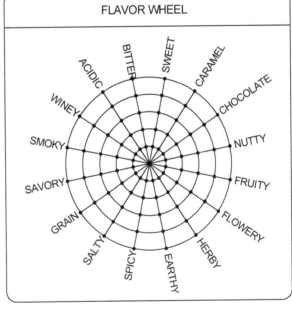

BITTER, SWEET, CARAMEL, CHOCOLATE, NUTTY, FRUITY, FLOWERY, HERBY, EARTHY, SPICY, SALTY, GRAIN, SAVORY, SMOKY, WINEY, ACIDIC

ADDITIONAL NOTES

FINAL RATING

APPEARANCE	☆☆☆☆☆
AROMA	☆☆☆☆☆
TASTE	☆☆☆☆☆
CREMA	☆☆☆☆☆
OVERALL RATING	☆☆☆☆☆

NAME

ROASTERY	BREW METHOD
GRIND	EXTRAS
ORIGIN	SAMPLED

SERVING TYPE

CASUAL	ESPRESSO	CAPPUCCINO	LATTE	MOCHA	MACCHIATO	OTHER
☐	☐	☐	☐	☐	☐	☐

COLOR

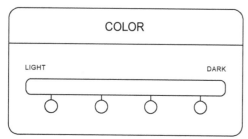

LIGHT   DARK

FLAVOR WHEEL

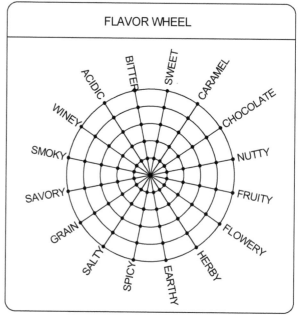

ACIDIC · BITTER · SWEET · CARAMEL · CHOCOLATE · NUTTY · FRUITY · FLOWERY · HERBY · EARTHY · SPICY · SALTY · GRAIN · SAVORY · SMOKY · WINEY

ADDITIONAL NOTES

FINAL RATING

APPEARANCE	☆☆☆☆☆
AROMA	☆☆☆☆☆
TASTE	☆☆☆☆☆
CREMA	☆☆☆☆☆
OVERALL RATING	☆☆☆☆☆

🫘 NAME	
📇 ROASTERY	🖥 BREW METHOD
⚙ GRIND	🧁 EXTRAS
🌍 ORIGIN	📅 SAMPLED

SERVING TYPE

CASUAL	ESPRESSO	CAPPUCCINO	LATTE	MOCHA	MACCHIATO	OTHER
☐	☐	☐	☐	☐	☐	☐

COLOR

LIGHT   DARK

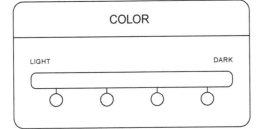

FLAVOR WHEEL

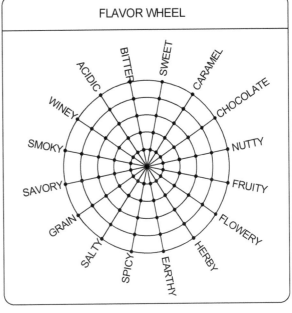

ACIDIC · BITTER · SWEET · CARAMEL · CHOCOLATE · NUTTY · FRUITY · FLOWERY · HERBY · EARTHY · SPICY · SALTY · GRAIN · SAVORY · SMOKY · WINEY

ADDITIONAL NOTES

FINAL RATING

🏵 APPEARANCE	☆☆☆☆☆
🌿 AROMA	☆☆☆☆☆
☕ TASTE	☆☆☆☆☆
💧 CREMA	☆☆☆☆☆
🖐 OVERALL RATING	☆☆☆☆☆

NAME

ROASTERY	BREW METHOD
GRIND	EXTRAS
ORIGIN	SAMPLED

SERVING TYPE

CASUAL	ESPRESSO	CAPPUCCINO	LATTE	MOCHA	MACCHIATO	OTHER
☐	☐	☐	☐	☐	☐	☐

COLOR

LIGHT   DARK

FLAVOR WHEEL

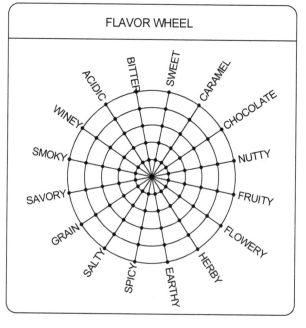

ACIDIC · BITTER · SWEET · CARAMEL · CHOCOLATE · WINEY · SMOKY · NUTTY · SAVORY · FRUITY · GRAIN · FLOWERY · SALTY · HERBY · SPICY · EARTHY

ADDITIONAL NOTES

FINAL RATING

APPEARANCE	☆☆☆☆☆
AROMA	☆☆☆☆☆
TASTE	☆☆☆☆☆
CREMA	☆☆☆☆☆
OVERALL RATING	☆☆☆☆☆

NAME

ROASTERY	BREW METHOD
GRIND	EXTRAS
ORIGIN	SAMPLED

SERVING TYPE

CASUAL	ESPRESSO	CAPPUCCINO	LATTE	MOCHA	MACCHIATO	OTHER
☐	☐	☐	☐	☐	☐	☐

COLOR

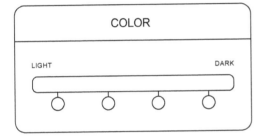

LIGHT   DARK

FLAVOR WHEEL

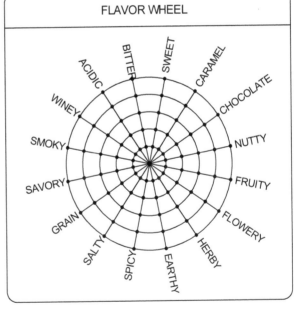

BITTER · SWEET · CARAMEL · CHOCOLATE · NUTTY · FRUITY · FLOWERY · HERBY · EARTHY · SPICY · SALTY · GRAIN · SAVORY · SMOKY · WINEY · ACIDIC

ADDITIONAL NOTES

FINAL RATING

APPEARANCE	☆☆☆☆☆
AROMA	☆☆☆☆☆
TASTE	☆☆☆☆☆
CREMA	☆☆☆☆☆
OVERALL RATING	☆☆☆☆☆

NAME

ROASTERY	BREW METHOD
GRIND	EXTRAS
ORIGIN	SAMPLED

SERVING TYPE

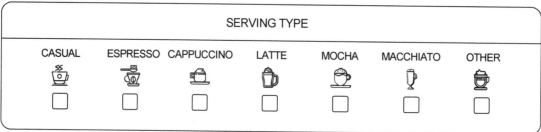

CASUAL	ESPRESSO	CAPPUCCINO	LATTE	MOCHA	MACCHIATO	OTHER
☐	☐	☐	☐	☐	☐	☐

COLOR

LIGHT   DARK

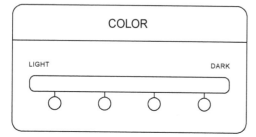

FLAVOR WHEEL

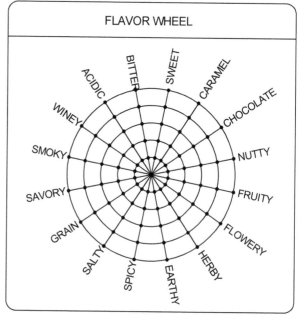

ACIDIC · BITTER · SWEET · CARAMEL · CHOCOLATE · WINEY · NUTTY · SMOKY · FRUITY · SAVORY · FLOWERY · GRAIN · HERBY · SALTY · SPICY · EARTHY

ADDITIONAL NOTES

FINAL RATING

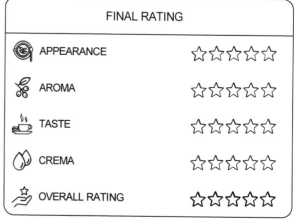

APPEARANCE	☆☆☆☆☆
AROMA	☆☆☆☆☆
TASTE	☆☆☆☆☆
CREMA	☆☆☆☆☆
OVERALL RATING	☆☆☆☆☆

NAME

ROASTERY	BREW METHOD
GRIND	EXTRAS
ORIGIN	SAMPLED

SERVING TYPE

CASUAL	ESPRESSO	CAPPUCCINO	LATTE	MOCHA	MACCHIATO	OTHER
☐	☐	☐	☐	☐	☐	☐

COLOR

LIGHT   DARK

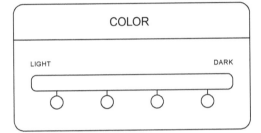

FLAVOR WHEEL

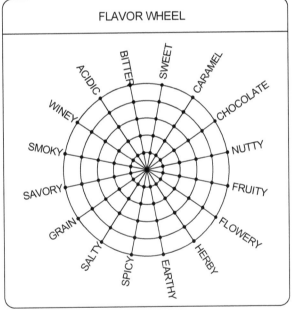

ADDITIONAL NOTES

FINAL RATING

APPEARANCE	☆☆☆☆☆
AROMA	☆☆☆☆☆
TASTE	☆☆☆☆☆
CREMA	☆☆☆☆☆
OVERALL RATING	☆☆☆☆☆

NAME

ROASTERY	BREW METHOD
GRIND	EXTRAS
ORIGIN	SAMPLED

SERVING TYPE

CASUAL	ESPRESSO	CAPPUCCINO	LATTE	MOCHA	MACCHIATO	OTHER
☐	☐	☐	☐	☐	☐	☐

COLOR

LIGHT   DARK

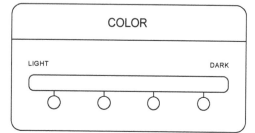

ADDITIONAL NOTES

FLAVOR WHEEL

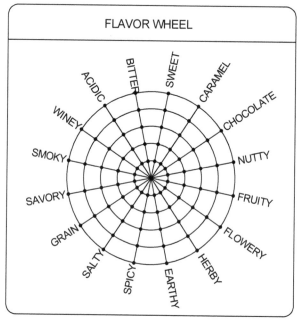

BITTER · SWEET · CARAMEL · ACIDIC · CHOCOLATE · WINEY · SMOKY · NUTTY · SAVORY · FRUITY · GRAIN · FLOWERY · SALTY · HERBY · SPICY · EARTHY

FINAL RATING

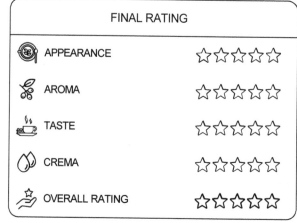

APPEARANCE	☆☆☆☆☆
AROMA	☆☆☆☆☆
TASTE	☆☆☆☆☆
CREMA	☆☆☆☆☆
OVERALL RATING	☆☆☆☆☆

NAME

ROASTERY	BREW METHOD
GRIND	EXTRAS
ORIGIN	SAMPLED

SERVING TYPE

CASUAL	ESPRESSO	CAPPUCCINO	LATTE	MOCHA	MACCHIATO	OTHER
☐	☐	☐	☐	☐	☐	☐

COLOR

LIGHT   DARK

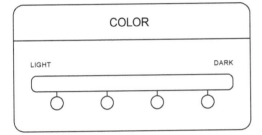

FLAVOR WHEEL

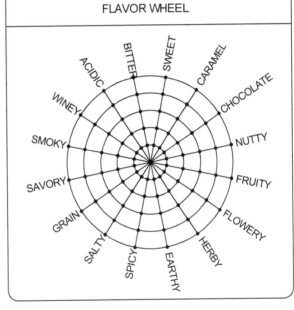

ADDITIONAL NOTES

FINAL RATING

APPEARANCE	☆☆☆☆☆
AROMA	☆☆☆☆☆
TASTE	☆☆☆☆☆
CREMA	☆☆☆☆☆
OVERALL RATING	☆☆☆☆☆

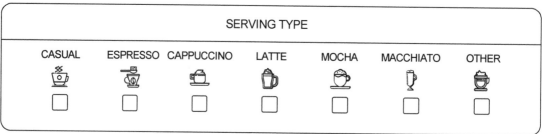 NAME	
ROASTERY	BREW METHOD
GRIND	EXTRAS
ORIGIN	SAMPLED

SERVING TYPE

CASUAL	ESPRESSO	CAPPUCCINO	LATTE	MOCHA	MACCHIATO	OTHER
☐	☐	☐	☐	☐	☐	☐

COLOR

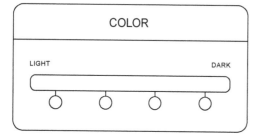

LIGHT · · · · · · DARK

FLAVOR WHEEL

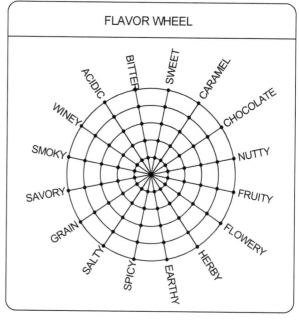

ACIDIC · BITTER · SWEET · CARAMEL · CHOCOLATE · NUTTY · FRUITY · FLOWERY · HERBY · EARTHY · SPICY · SALTY · GRAIN · SAVORY · SMOKY · WINEY

ADDITIONAL NOTES

FINAL RATING

APPEARANCE	☆☆☆☆☆
AROMA	☆☆☆☆☆
TASTE	☆☆☆☆☆
CREMA	☆☆☆☆☆
OVERALL RATING	☆☆☆☆☆

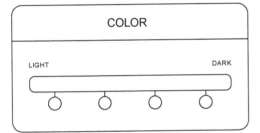 NAME	
ROASTERY	BREW METHOD
GRIND	EXTRAS
ORIGIN	SAMPLED

SERVING TYPE

CASUAL	ESPRESSO	CAPPUCCINO	LATTE	MOCHA	MACCHIATO	OTHER
☐	☐	☐	☐	☐	☐	☐

COLOR

LIGHT   DARK

○   ○   ○   ○

FLAVOR WHEEL

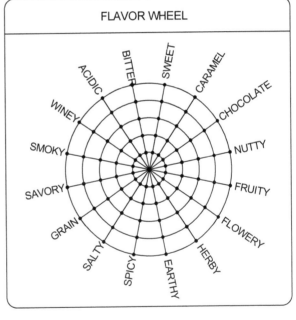

ACIDIC — BITTER — SWEET — CARAMEL — CHOCOLATE — NUTTY — FRUITY — FLOWERY — HERBY — EARTHY — SPICY — SALTY — GRAIN — SAVORY — SMOKY — WINEY

ADDITIONAL NOTES

FINAL RATING

APPEARANCE	☆☆☆☆☆
AROMA	☆☆☆☆☆
TASTE	☆☆☆☆☆
CREMA	☆☆☆☆☆
OVERALL RATING	☆☆☆☆☆

NAME	
ROASTERY	BREW METHOD
GRIND	EXTRAS
ORIGIN	SAMPLED

SERVING TYPE

CASUAL	ESPRESSO	CAPPUCCINO	LATTE	MOCHA	MACCHIATO	OTHER
☐	☐	☐	☐	☐	☐	☐

COLOR

LIGHT   DARK

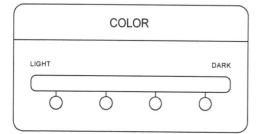

FLAVOR WHEEL

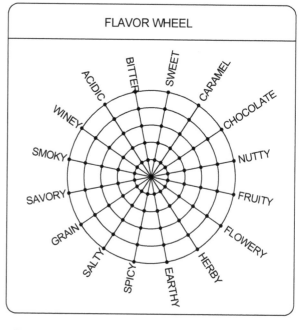

ACIDIC · BITTER · SWEET · CARAMEL · CHOCOLATE · NUTTY · FRUITY · FLOWERY · HERBY · EARTHY · SPICY · SALTY · GRAIN · SAVORY · SMOKY · WINEY

ADDITIONAL NOTES

FINAL RATING

APPEARANCE	☆☆☆☆☆
AROMA	☆☆☆☆☆
TASTE	☆☆☆☆☆
CREMA	☆☆☆☆☆
OVERALL RATING	☆☆☆☆☆

NAME

ROASTERY	BREW METHOD
GRIND	EXTRAS
ORIGIN	SAMPLED

SERVING TYPE

CASUAL	ESPRESSO	CAPPUCCINO	LATTE	MOCHA	MACCHIATO	OTHER
☐	☐	☐	☐	☐	☐	☐

COLOR

LIGHT   DARK

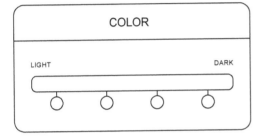

FLAVOR WHEEL

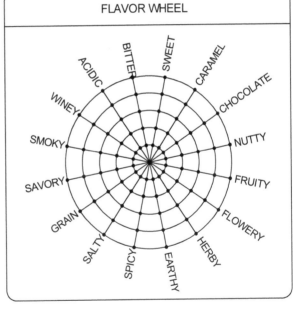

BITTER · SWEET · CARAMEL · CHOCOLATE · NUTTY · FRUITY · FLOWERY · HERBY · EARTHY · SPICY · SALTY · GRAIN · SAVORY · SMOKY · WINEY · ACIDIC

ADDITIONAL NOTES

FINAL RATING

APPEARANCE	☆☆☆☆☆
AROMA	☆☆☆☆☆
TASTE	☆☆☆☆☆
CREMA	☆☆☆☆☆
OVERALL RATING	☆☆☆☆☆

NAME

ROASTERY	BREW METHOD
GRIND	EXTRAS
ORIGIN	SAMPLED

SERVING TYPE

CASUAL	ESPRESSO	CAPPUCCINO	LATTE	MOCHA	MACCHIATO	OTHER
☐	☐	☐	☐	☐	☐	☐

COLOR

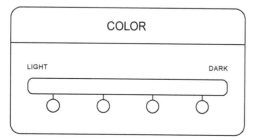

LIGHT   DARK

ADDITIONAL NOTES

FLAVOR WHEEL

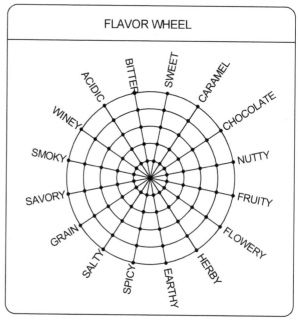

ACIDIC · BITTER · SWEET · CARAMEL · CHOCOLATE · NUTTY · FRUITY · FLOWERY · HERBY · EARTHY · SPICY · SALTY · GRAIN · SAVORY · SMOKY · WINEY

FINAL RATING

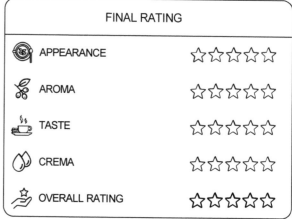

APPEARANCE	☆☆☆☆☆
AROMA	☆☆☆☆☆
TASTE	☆☆☆☆☆
CREMA	☆☆☆☆☆
OVERALL RATING	☆☆☆☆☆

🫘 NAME	
📇 ROASTERY	🖥 BREW METHOD
⚙ GRIND	🧁 EXTRAS
🌍 ORIGIN	📅 SAMPLED

SERVING TYPE

CASUAL	ESPRESSO	CAPPUCCINO	LATTE	MOCHA	MACCHIATO	OTHER
☐	☐	☐	☐	☐	☐	☐

COLOR

LIGHT   DARK

○   ○   ○   ○

FLAVOR WHEEL

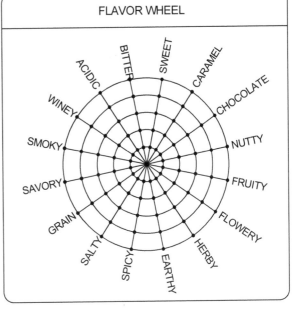

ADDITIONAL NOTES

FINAL RATING

🌀 APPEARANCE	☆☆☆☆☆
🌿 AROMA	☆☆☆☆☆
☕ TASTE	☆☆☆☆☆
💧 CREMA	☆☆☆☆☆
🤲 OVERALL RATING	☆☆☆☆☆

NAME

ROASTERY	BREW METHOD
GRIND	EXTRAS
ORIGIN	SAMPLED

SERVING TYPE

CASUAL	ESPRESSO	CAPPUCCINO	LATTE	MOCHA	MACCHIATO	OTHER
☐	☐	☐	☐	☐	☐	☐

COLOR

LIGHT   DARK

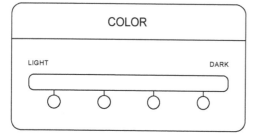

ADDITIONAL NOTES

FLAVOR WHEEL

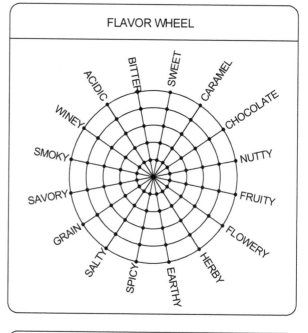

FINAL RATING

APPEARANCE	☆☆☆☆☆
AROMA	☆☆☆☆☆
TASTE	☆☆☆☆☆
CREMA	☆☆☆☆☆
OVERALL RATING	☆☆☆☆☆

NAME

ROASTERY	BREW METHOD
GRIND	EXTRAS
ORIGIN	SAMPLED

SERVING TYPE

CASUAL	ESPRESSO	CAPPUCCINO	LATTE	MOCHA	MACCHIATO	OTHER
☐	☐	☐	☐	☐	☐	☐

COLOR

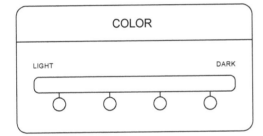

LIGHT — DARK

FLAVOR WHEEL

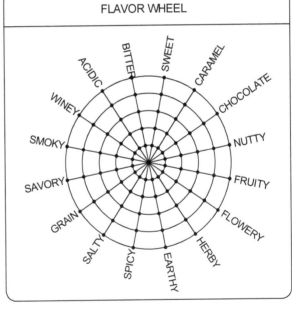

ACIDIC · BITTER · SWEET · CARAMEL · CHOCOLATE · NUTTY · FRUITY · FLOWERY · HERBY · EARTHY · SPICY · SALTY · GRAIN · SAVORY · SMOKY · WINEY

ADDITIONAL NOTES

FINAL RATING

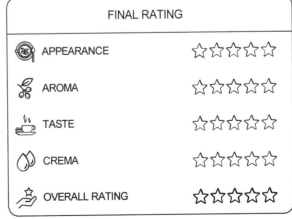

APPEARANCE	☆☆☆☆☆
AROMA	☆☆☆☆☆
TASTE	☆☆☆☆☆
CREMA	☆☆☆☆☆
OVERALL RATING	☆☆☆☆☆

NAME

ROASTERY	BREW METHOD
GRIND	EXTRAS
ORIGIN	SAMPLED

SERVING TYPE

CASUAL	ESPRESSO	CAPPUCCINO	LATTE	MOCHA	MACCHIATO	OTHER
☐	☐	☐	☐	☐	☐	☐

COLOR

LIGHT   DARK

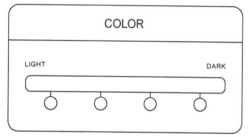

FLAVOR WHEEL

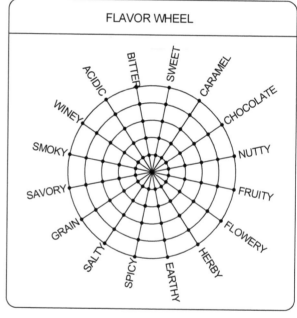

BITTER · SWEET · CARAMEL · CHOCOLATE · NUTTY · FRUITY · FLOWERY · HERBY · EARTHY · SPICY · SALTY · GRAIN · SAVORY · SMOKY · WINEY · ACIDIC

ADDITIONAL NOTES

FINAL RATING

APPEARANCE	☆☆☆☆☆
AROMA	☆☆☆☆☆
TASTE	☆☆☆☆☆
CREMA	☆☆☆☆☆
OVERALL RATING	☆☆☆☆☆

NAME

ROASTERY	BREW METHOD
GRIND	EXTRAS
ORIGIN	SAMPLED

SERVING TYPE

CASUAL	ESPRESSO	CAPPUCCINO	LATTE	MOCHA	MACCHIATO	OTHER
☐	☐	☐	☐	☐	☐	☐

COLOR

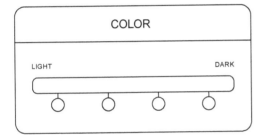

LIGHT   DARK

FLAVOR WHEEL

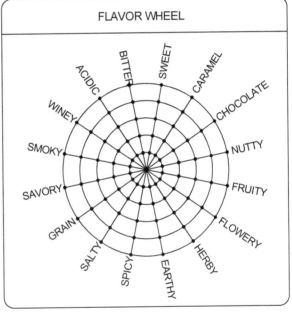

ADDITIONAL NOTES

FINAL RATING

APPEARANCE	☆☆☆☆☆
AROMA	☆☆☆☆☆
TASTE	☆☆☆☆☆
CREMA	☆☆☆☆☆
OVERALL RATING	☆☆☆☆☆

NAME

ROASTERY	BREW METHOD
GRIND	EXTRAS
ORIGIN	SAMPLED

SERVING TYPE

CASUAL	ESPRESSO	CAPPUCCINO	LATTE	MOCHA	MACCHIATO	OTHER
☐	☐	☐	☐	☐	☐	☐

COLOR

LIGHT   DARK

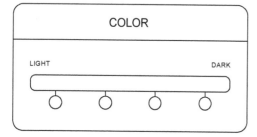

FLAVOR WHEEL

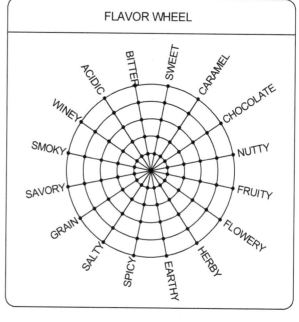

ACIDIC · BITTER · SWEET · CARAMEL · CHOCOLATE · NUTTY · FRUITY · FLOWERY · HERBY · EARTHY · SPICY · SALTY · GRAIN · SAVORY · SMOKY · WINEY

ADDITIONAL NOTES

FINAL RATING

APPEARANCE	☆☆☆☆☆
AROMA	☆☆☆☆☆
TASTE	☆☆☆☆☆
CREMA	☆☆☆☆☆
OVERALL RATING	☆☆☆☆☆

NAME

ROASTERY	BREW METHOD
GRIND	EXTRAS
ORIGIN	SAMPLED

SERVING TYPE

CASUAL	ESPRESSO	CAPPUCCINO	LATTE	MOCHA	MACCHIATO	OTHER
☐	☐	☐	☐	☐	☐	☐

COLOR

LIGHT   DARK

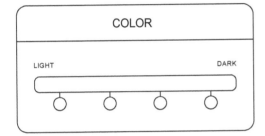

FLAVOR WHEEL

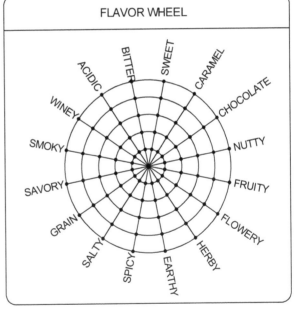

BITTER, SWEET, CARAMEL, CHOCOLATE, NUTTY, FRUITY, FLOWERY, HERBY, EARTHY, SPICY, SALTY, GRAIN, SAVORY, SMOKY, WINEY, ACIDIC

ADDITIONAL NOTES

FINAL RATING

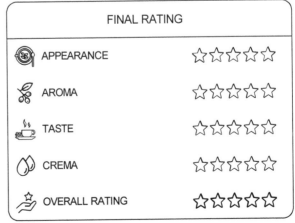

APPEARANCE	☆☆☆☆☆
AROMA	☆☆☆☆☆
TASTE	☆☆☆☆☆
CREMA	☆☆☆☆☆
OVERALL RATING	☆☆☆☆☆

NAME

ROASTERY	BREW METHOD
GRIND	EXTRAS
ORIGIN	SAMPLED

SERVING TYPE

CASUAL	ESPRESSO	CAPPUCCINO	LATTE	MOCHA	MACCHIATO	OTHER
☐	☐	☐	☐	☐	☐	☐

COLOR

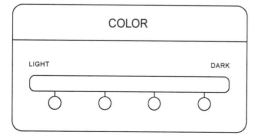

LIGHT   DARK

FLAVOR WHEEL

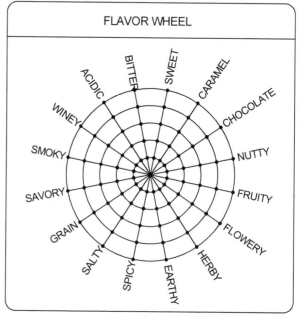

ACIDIC · BITTER · SWEET · CARAMEL · CHOCOLATE · NUTTY · FRUITY · FLOWERY · HERBY · EARTHY · SPICY · SALTY · GRAIN · SAVORY · SMOKY · WINEY

ADDITIONAL NOTES

FINAL RATING

APPEARANCE	☆☆☆☆☆
AROMA	☆☆☆☆☆
TASTE	☆☆☆☆☆
CREMA	☆☆☆☆☆
OVERALL RATING	☆☆☆☆☆

NAME	
ROASTERY	BREW METHOD
GRIND	EXTRAS
ORIGIN	SAMPLED

SERVING TYPE

CASUAL	ESPRESSO	CAPPUCCINO	LATTE	MOCHA	MACCHIATO	OTHER
☐	☐	☐	☐	☐	☐	☐

COLOR

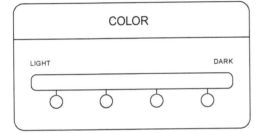

LIGHT   DARK

FLAVOR WHEEL

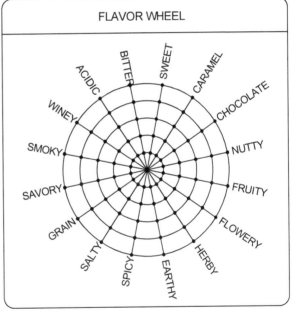

BITTER · SWEET · CARAMEL · CHOCOLATE · NUTTY · FRUITY · FLOWERY · HERBY · EARTHY · SPICY · SALTY · GRAIN · SAVORY · SMOKY · WINEY · ACIDIC

ADDITIONAL NOTES

FINAL RATING

APPEARANCE	☆☆☆☆☆	
AROMA	☆☆☆☆☆	
TASTE	☆☆☆☆☆	
CREMA	☆☆☆☆☆	
OVERALL RATING	☆☆☆☆☆	

🫘 NAME	
📇 ROASTERY	☕ BREW METHOD
⚙️ GRIND	🧁 EXTRAS
🌐 ORIGIN	📅 SAMPLED

SERVING TYPE

CASUAL	ESPRESSO	CAPPUCCINO	LATTE	MOCHA	MACCHIATO	OTHER
☐	☐	☐	☐	☐	☐	☐

COLOR

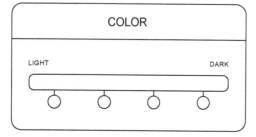

LIGHT ⟶ DARK

ADDITIONAL NOTES

FLAVOR WHEEL

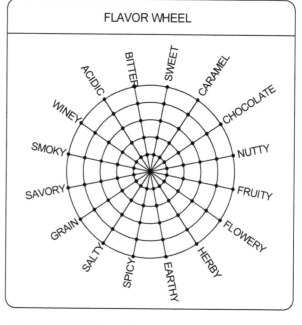

ACIDIC · BITTER · SWEET · CARAMEL · CHOCOLATE · NUTTY · FRUITY · FLOWERY · HERBY · EARTHY · SPICY · SALTY · GRAIN · SAVORY · SMOKY · WINEY

FINAL RATING

🍩 APPEARANCE	☆☆☆☆☆
🌿 AROMA	☆☆☆☆☆
☕ TASTE	☆☆☆☆☆
💧 CREMA	☆☆☆☆☆
✨ OVERALL RATING	☆☆☆☆☆

NAME

ROASTERY	BREW METHOD
GRIND	EXTRAS
ORIGIN	SAMPLED

SERVING TYPE

CASUAL	ESPRESSO	CAPPUCCINO	LATTE	MOCHA	MACCHIATO	OTHER
☐	☐	☐	☐	☐	☐	☐

COLOR

LIGHT   DARK

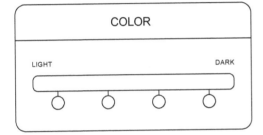

FLAVOR WHEEL

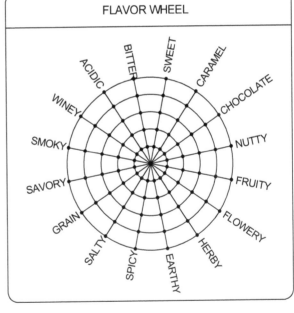

ADDITIONAL NOTES

FINAL RATING

APPEARANCE	☆☆☆☆☆
AROMA	☆☆☆☆☆
TASTE	☆☆☆☆☆
CREMA	☆☆☆☆☆
OVERALL RATING	☆☆☆☆☆

NAME

ROASTERY	BREW METHOD
GRIND	EXTRAS
ORIGIN	SAMPLED

SERVING TYPE

CASUAL	ESPRESSO	CAPPUCCINO	LATTE	MOCHA	MACCHIATO	OTHER
☐	☐	☐	☐	☐	☐	☐

COLOR

LIGHT — DARK

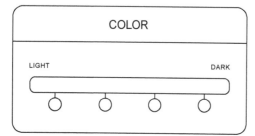

FLAVOR WHEEL

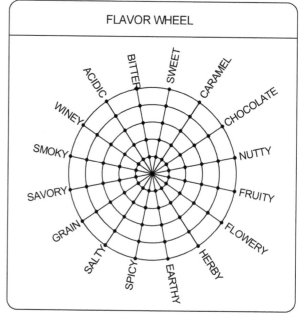

ACIDIC, BITTER, SWEET, CARAMEL, CHOCOLATE, NUTTY, FRUITY, FLOWERY, HERBY, EARTHY, SPICY, SALTY, GRAIN, SAVORY, SMOKY, WINEY

ADDITIONAL NOTES

FINAL RATING

APPEARANCE	☆☆☆☆☆
AROMA	☆☆☆☆☆
TASTE	☆☆☆☆☆
CREMA	☆☆☆☆☆
OVERALL RATING	☆☆☆☆☆

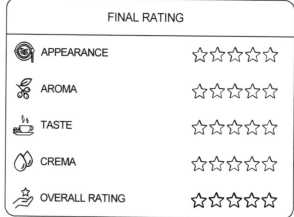

NAME

ROASTERY	BREW METHOD
GRIND	EXTRAS
ORIGIN	SAMPLED

SERVING TYPE

CASUAL	ESPRESSO	CAPPUCCINO	LATTE	MOCHA	MACCHIATO	OTHER
☐	☐	☐	☐	☐	☐	☐

COLOR

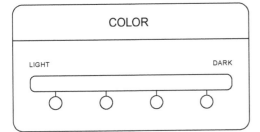

LIGHT   DARK

ADDITIONAL NOTES

FLAVOR WHEEL

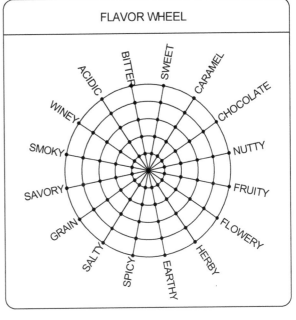

BITTER · SWEET · CARAMEL · CHOCOLATE · ACIDIC · WINEY · NUTTY · SMOKY · FRUITY · SAVORY · FLOWERY · GRAIN · HERBY · SALTY · SPICY · EARTHY

FINAL RATING

APPEARANCE	☆☆☆☆☆
AROMA	☆☆☆☆☆
TASTE	☆☆☆☆☆
CREMA	☆☆☆☆☆
OVERALL RATING	☆☆☆☆☆

NAME

ROASTERY	BREW METHOD
GRIND	EXTRAS
ORIGIN	SAMPLED

SERVING TYPE

CASUAL	ESPRESSO	CAPPUCCINO	LATTE	MOCHA	MACCHIATO	OTHER
☐	☐	☐	☐	☐	☐	☐

COLOR

LIGHT — DARK

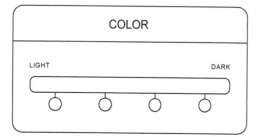

ADDITIONAL NOTES

FLAVOR WHEEL

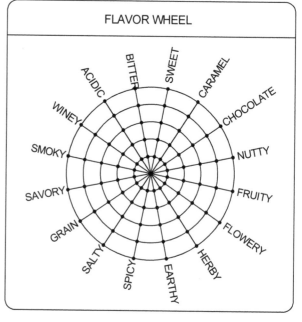

ACIDIC · BITTER · SWEET · CARAMEL · CHOCOLATE · NUTTY · FRUITY · FLOWERY · HERBY · EARTHY · SPICY · SALTY · GRAIN · SAVORY · SMOKY · WINEY

FINAL RATING

APPEARANCE	☆☆☆☆☆
AROMA	☆☆☆☆☆
TASTE	☆☆☆☆☆
CREMA	☆☆☆☆☆
OVERALL RATING	☆☆☆☆☆

NAME

ROASTERY	BREW METHOD
GRIND	EXTRAS
ORIGIN	SAMPLED

SERVING TYPE

CASUAL	ESPRESSO	CAPPUCCINO	LATTE	MOCHA	MACCHIATO	OTHER
☐	☐	☐	☐	☐	☐	☐

COLOR

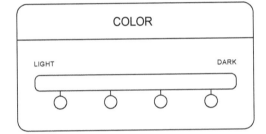

LIGHT　　　　　　　　　　　DARK

FLAVOR WHEEL

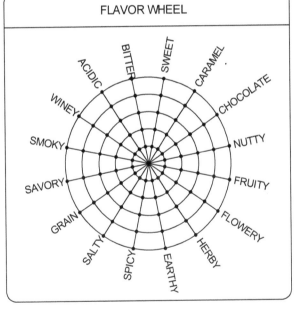

ADDITIONAL NOTES

FINAL RATING

APPEARANCE	☆☆☆☆☆
AROMA	☆☆☆☆☆
TASTE	☆☆☆☆☆
CREMA	☆☆☆☆☆
OVERALL RATING	☆☆☆☆☆

NAME

ROASTERY	BREW METHOD
GRIND	EXTRAS
ORIGIN	SAMPLED

SERVING TYPE

CASUAL	ESPRESSO	CAPPUCCINO	LATTE	MOCHA	MACCHIATO	OTHER
☐	☐	☐	☐	☐	☐	☐

COLOR

LIGHT — DARK

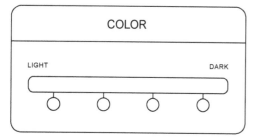

FLAVOR WHEEL

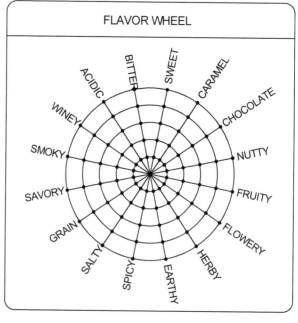

BITTER · SWEET · CARAMEL · ACIDIC · CHOCOLATE · WINEY · NUTTY · SMOKY · FRUITY · SAVORY · FLOWERY · GRAIN · HERBY · SALTY · EARTHY · SPICY

ADDITIONAL NOTES

FINAL RATING

APPEARANCE	☆☆☆☆☆
AROMA	☆☆☆☆☆
TASTE	☆☆☆☆☆
CREMA	☆☆☆☆☆
OVERALL RATING	☆☆☆☆☆

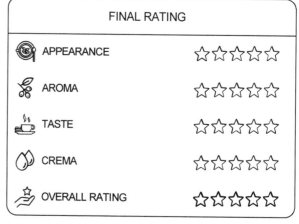

NAME

ROASTERY	BREW METHOD
GRIND	EXTRAS
ORIGIN	SAMPLED

SERVING TYPE

CASUAL	ESPRESSO	CAPPUCCINO	LATTE	MOCHA	MACCHIATO	OTHER
☐	☐	☐	☐	☐	☐	☐

COLOR

LIGHT   DARK

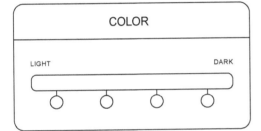

FLAVOR WHEEL

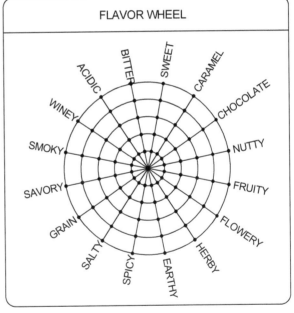

BITTER, SWEET, CARAMEL, ACIDIC, CHOCOLATE, WINEY, NUTTY, SMOKY, FRUITY, SAVORY, FLOWERY, GRAIN, HERBY, SALTY, SPICY, EARTHY

ADDITIONAL NOTES

FINAL RATING

APPEARANCE	☆☆☆☆☆
AROMA	☆☆☆☆☆
TASTE	☆☆☆☆☆
CREMA	☆☆☆☆☆
OVERALL RATING	☆☆☆☆☆

NAME

ROASTERY	BREW METHOD
GRIND	EXTRAS
ORIGIN	SAMPLED

SERVING TYPE

CASUAL	ESPRESSO	CAPPUCCINO	LATTE	MOCHA	MACCHIATO	OTHER
☐	☐	☐	☐	☐	☐	☐

COLOR

LIGHT   DARK

FLAVOR WHEEL

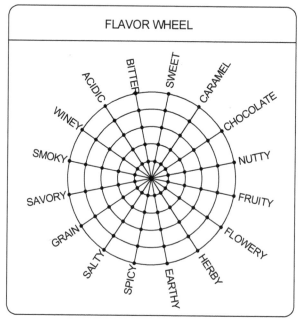

ADDITIONAL NOTES

FINAL RATING

APPEARANCE	☆☆☆☆☆
AROMA	☆☆☆☆☆
TASTE	☆☆☆☆☆
CREMA	☆☆☆☆☆
OVERALL RATING	☆☆☆☆☆

NAME

ROASTERY	BREW METHOD
GRIND	EXTRAS
ORIGIN	SAMPLED

SERVING TYPE

CASUAL	ESPRESSO	CAPPUCCINO	LATTE	MOCHA	MACCHIATO	OTHER
☐	☐	☐	☐	☐	☐	☐

COLOR

LIGHT   DARK

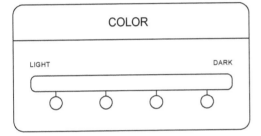

FLAVOR WHEEL

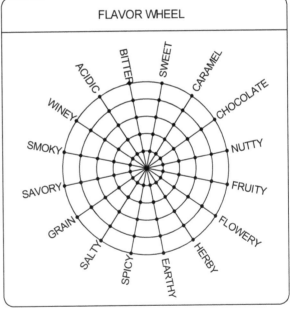

BITTER · SWEET · CARAMEL · CHOCOLATE · NUTTY · FRUITY · FLOWERY · HERBY · EARTHY · SPICY · SALTY · GRAIN · SAVORY · SMOKY · WINEY · ACIDIC

ADDITIONAL NOTES

FINAL RATING

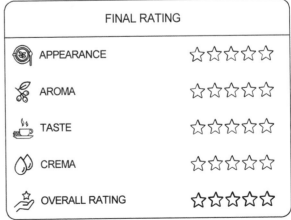

APPEARANCE	☆☆☆☆☆
AROMA	☆☆☆☆☆
TASTE	☆☆☆☆☆
CREMA	☆☆☆☆☆
OVERALL RATING	☆☆☆☆☆

NAME

ROASTERY	BREW METHOD
GRIND	EXTRAS
ORIGIN	SAMPLED

SERVING TYPE

CASUAL	ESPRESSO	CAPPUCCINO	LATTE	MOCHA	MACCHIATO	OTHER
☐	☐	☐	☐	☐	☐	☐

COLOR

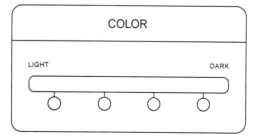

LIGHT   DARK

ADDITIONAL NOTES

FLAVOR WHEEL

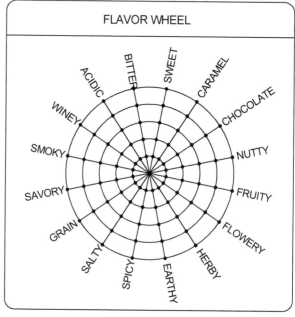

FINAL RATING

APPEARANCE		☆☆☆☆☆
AROMA		☆☆☆☆☆
TASTE		☆☆☆☆☆
CREMA		☆☆☆☆☆
OVERALL RATING		☆☆☆☆☆

NAME

ROASTERY	BREW METHOD
GRIND	EXTRAS
ORIGIN	SAMPLED

SERVING TYPE

CASUAL	ESPRESSO	CAPPUCCINO	LATTE	MOCHA	MACCHIATO	OTHER
☐	☐	☐	☐	☐	☐	☐

COLOR

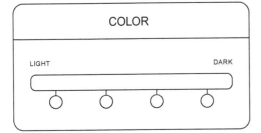

LIGHT   DARK

FLAVOR WHEEL

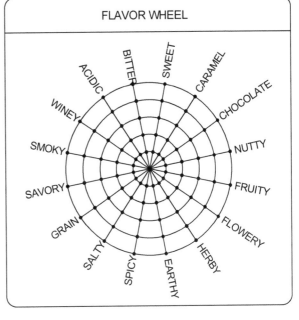

ACIDIC · BITTER · SWEET · CARAMEL · CHOCOLATE · NUTTY · FRUITY · FLOWERY · HERBY · EARTHY · SPICY · SALTY · GRAIN · SAVORY · SMOKY · WINEY

ADDITIONAL NOTES

FINAL RATING

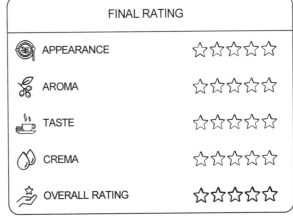

APPEARANCE	☆☆☆☆☆
AROMA	☆☆☆☆☆
TASTE	☆☆☆☆☆
CREMA	☆☆☆☆☆
OVERALL RATING	☆☆☆☆☆

NAME

ROASTERY	BREW METHOD
GRIND	EXTRAS
ORIGIN	SAMPLED

SERVING TYPE

CASUAL	ESPRESSO	CAPPUCCINO	LATTE	MOCHA	MACCHIATO	OTHER
☐	☐	☐	☐	☐	☐	☐

COLOR

LIGHT   DARK

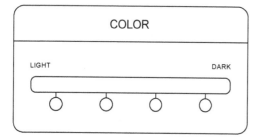

FLAVOR WHEEL

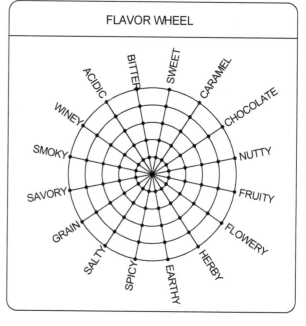

BITTER · SWEET · CARAMEL · CHOCOLATE · NUTTY · FRUITY · FLOWERY · HERBY · EARTHY · SPICY · SALTY · GRAIN · SAVORY · SMOKY · WINEY · ACIDIC

ADDITIONAL NOTES

FINAL RATING

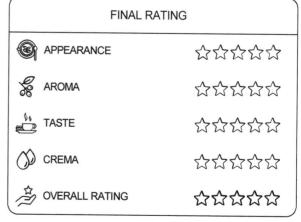

APPEARANCE	☆☆☆☆☆
AROMA	☆☆☆☆☆
TASTE	☆☆☆☆☆
CREMA	☆☆☆☆☆
OVERALL RATING	☆☆☆☆☆

NAME	
ROASTERY	BREW METHOD
GRIND	EXTRAS
ORIGIN	SAMPLED

SERVING TYPE

CASUAL	ESPRESSO	CAPPUCCINO	LATTE	MOCHA	MACCHIATO	OTHER
☐	☐	☐	☐	☐	☐	☐

COLOR

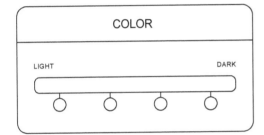

LIGHT — DARK

FLAVOR WHEEL

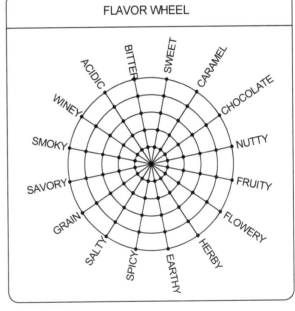

ACIDIC · BITTER · SWEET · CARAMEL · CHOCOLATE · NUTTY · FRUITY · FLOWERY · HERBY · EARTHY · SPICY · SALTY · GRAIN · SAVORY · SMOKY · WINEY

ADDITIONAL NOTES

FINAL RATING

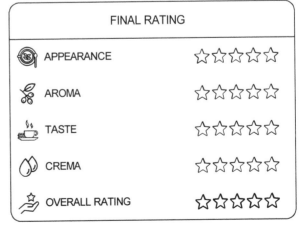

APPEARANCE ☆☆☆☆☆

AROMA ☆☆☆☆☆

TASTE ☆☆☆☆☆

CREMA ☆☆☆☆☆

OVERALL RATING ☆☆☆☆☆

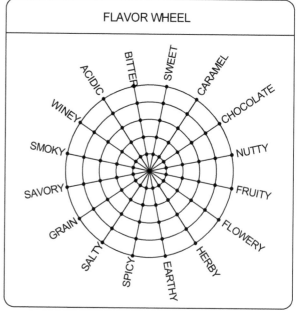 NAME	
🗃 ROASTERY	☕ BREW METHOD
⚙ GRIND	🧁 EXTRAS
🌍 ORIGIN	📅 SAMPLED

SERVING TYPE

CASUAL	ESPRESSO	CAPPUCCINO	LATTE	MOCHA	MACCHIATO	OTHER
☕	☕	☕	🥤	☕	☕	☕
☐	☐	☐	☐	☐	☐	☐

COLOR

LIGHT   DARK

◯   ◯   ◯   ◯

FLAVOR WHEEL

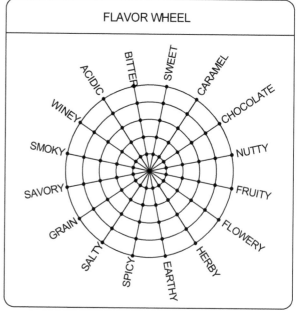

ADDITIONAL NOTES

FINAL RATING

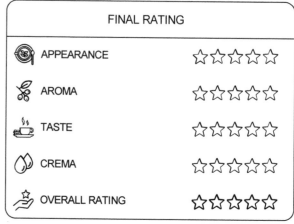

🔖 APPEARANCE	☆☆☆☆☆
🌿 AROMA	☆☆☆☆☆
☕ TASTE	☆☆☆☆☆
💧 CREMA	☆☆☆☆☆
✋ OVERALL RATING	☆☆☆☆☆

NAME

ROASTERY	BREW METHOD
GRIND	EXTRAS
ORIGIN	SAMPLED

SERVING TYPE

CASUAL	ESPRESSO	CAPPUCCINO	LATTE	MOCHA	MACCHIATO	OTHER
☐	☐	☐	☐	☐	☐	☐

COLOR

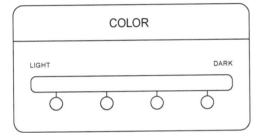

LIGHT — DARK

FLAVOR WHEEL

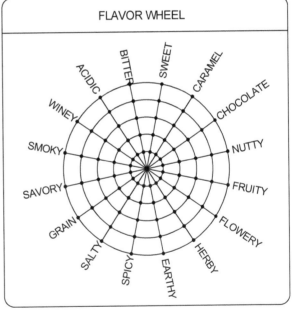

ACIDIC · BITTER · SWEET · CARAMEL · CHOCOLATE · NUTTY · FRUITY · FLOWERY · HERBY · EARTHY · SPICY · SALTY · GRAIN · SAVORY · SMOKY · WINEY

ADDITIONAL NOTES

FINAL RATING

APPEARANCE	☆☆☆☆☆
AROMA	☆☆☆☆☆
TASTE	☆☆☆☆☆
CREMA	☆☆☆☆☆
OVERALL RATING	☆☆☆☆☆

✿ NAME	
📚 ROASTERY	☕ BREW METHOD
⚙ GRIND	🧁 EXTRAS
🌍 ORIGIN	📅 SAMPLED

SERVING TYPE

CASUAL	ESPRESSO	CAPPUCCINO	LATTE	MOCHA	MACCHIATO	OTHER
☐	☐	☐	☐	☐	☐	☐

COLOR

LIGHT · DARK

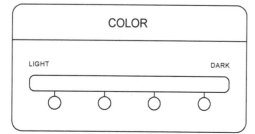

ADDITIONAL NOTES

FLAVOR WHEEL

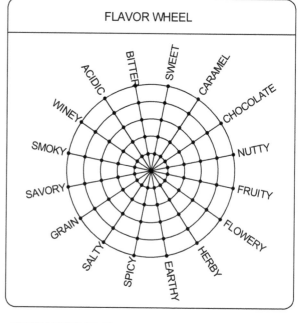

ACIDIC · BITTER · SWEET · CARAMEL · CHOCOLATE · NUTTY · FRUITY · FLOWERY · HERBY · EARTHY · SPICY · SALTY · GRAIN · SAVORY · SMOKY · WINEY

FINAL RATING

🐾 APPEARANCE	☆☆☆☆☆
🌿 AROMA	☆☆☆☆☆
☕ TASTE	☆☆☆☆☆
💧 CREMA	☆☆☆☆☆
✨ OVERALL RATING	☆☆☆☆☆

Lightning Source UK Ltd.
Milton Keynes UK
UKHW030632070820
367857UK00008B/1185